CREATING COMMUNITY

SECRETS *Savored*

THROUGH SIMPLE HOSPITALITY

UNDISTRACTED
Devotion

UNDISTRACTED
Devotion

BOOK THREE · WORKBOOK

DIANNE LYNN DOUGHARTY

HIGH BRIDGE BOOKS
HOUSTON

SECRETS SAVORED
Book Three Workbook: Undistracted Devotion
Copyright © 2021 by Dianne Lynn Dougharty
All rights reserved.

Other Bible Translations quoted in this book are listed on page 277, which hereby becomes part of this copyright page.

Library of Congress Control Number: 2012945608
ISBN: 978-1-946615-79-4

Book Design: *Studio B Print & Design*, Tyler Bedwell

Cover Photo: Will Porada

Printed in the United States of America
U.S. Printing History

First Edition: August 2015

High Bridge Books
Houston, TX

Requests for Information should be addressed to:

Secrets Savored, Inc.
P.O. Box 2257
Cordova, Tennessee 38088

LEADER GUIDE:
The companion Leader Guide with weekly lessons is available on our website at www.secretssavored.org. Go to "Select a Page" and click on shop.

TO ORDER MATERIALS:
To purchase participant workbooks, go to the website at www.secretssavored.org. You will need one book per participant.

Angela and Kelly ...

You are the joy of my heart!
You have matured into beautiful, godly women.
Your devotion to the Lord and the radiance of His Holy Spirit
are evident in your lives in the way you love others.
How blessed I am to be your mom!

Those who look to him ... will be radiant with joy.
Psalm 34:5 NLT

Contents

Weekly Menus

WEEK ONE MENU | 30

Mango Salsa Chicken
Black Rice
Oven Roasted Green Beans
Brownie Cheesecake Trifle

WEEK TWO MENU | 57

Baked Ziti with Italian Sausage
Simple Italian Salad
Lemon Fluff/Coconut Lemon Bars

WEEK THREE MENU | 79

Honey Pork Tenderloin
Golden Potato Casserole
Green Peas with Pine Nuts
Toffee Ice Cream Dessert with Chocolate Sauce

WEEK FOUR MENU | 104

Santa Fe Taco Soup
Joy's Mexican Cornbread
Old-Fashioned Banana Pudding

WEEK FIVE MENU | 128

Spinach and Bacon Quiche
Fresh Fruit
Dianne's Cheesy Garlic Grits
Lemon Blueberry Muffins

WEEK SIX MENU | 151

Roast Beef Sliders with Chipotle Sauce
Sweet Potato Fries with a Kick
Jumbo Chocolate Chip Cookies
Milky Way Ice Cream

INTRODUCTION
to Secrets Savored

I love the word *devotion*. It is feminine, rich, deep, and lush. Who doesn't desire for someone to be devoted to them? Devotion means steadfast, attentive, and having a love, loyalty, or enthusiasm for a person, activity, or cause. When thinking of an antonym for devotion, I think of *distraction*, which means a hindrance or a thing that prevents someone from giving full attention to something.

So, what is it that affects our devotion toward important things in our lives, like those we love? The answer is **distractions**! John Bloom described **distraction** this way in an article: "**Distraction**, at least the dangerous kind I'm referring to, is shifting our attention from something of greater importance to something of lesser importance."[1]

We all have things of **lesser importance** in our lives that distract us from the things of **greater importance**.

Unfortunately, **distracted** would describe me more often than not! I seem to find numerous **distractions**, things that steal away my devotion.

How many times have I thought that I should go visit or send a note to a friend or someone in a difficult circumstance in life, yet I let things of **lesser importance** keep me from doing it?

How many times have I walked into a store intending to purchase one item only to get distracted by the **lesser** but beautiful things around me and come out with a bag filled with stuff?

How many times have I sat down in my corner chair to have my quiet time with the Lord and allowed my iPhone or the laundry to distract me from focusing my attention on the Father and His Word?

I did not realize just how **distracted** I was by the **less important** things in life until the fall of 2007 when my world was turned upside down. God began to shed light on the **distractions** in my life—my lack of devotion to the things of **greater importance**.

It was September, just three months after my husband, Mark, had stepped away from his ministry job. We felt clearly that God was leading us away, just as clearly as we had felt the Lord lead us there eleven years prior. Mark was in for a yearly physical when his doctor asked how he was feeling. He told him he was feeling great except for one thing. For some months, he had noticed that his balance was off. He had fallen while running that spring, which had never happened before and stairs were becoming a challenge for him.

His doctor completed the exam; everything looked great. But, just in case, he ordered a CT scan. A few days later, he called Mark and explained the results of the test. They discovered that he had Cerebellar Atrophy, a very rare neurological condition. The cerebellum was shrinking prematurely, which was causing problems. We were told that Cerebellar Atrophy was a degenerative disease and could possibly result in a more invasive diagnosis of Multiple System Atrophy (MSA), which did occur a few years later.

The news was devastating for us. At the time, I was fifty-one, and Mark was fifty-six. Our girls were married and beginning their families. This was not at all the way we thought life was going to go. On the

---

[1] John Bloom, *Lord, Deliver Me from Distractions* (*desiringGod.org*, December 6, 2016).

journey that spanned eleven years, God brought to light many **distractions** in my life, things of **lesser importance**, that were harming my devotion to Him.

John Bloom proceeds in his article to say, "We're becoming conditioned to **distraction**, and it's harming our ability to listen and think carefully, to be still, to pray, and to meditate. Which means it is a spiritual danger, an evil from which we need God's deliverance."[2]

I was so conditioned to the **distractions**, the **lesser things**, in my life that I could not see the harm they were doing to me spiritually. But, because God loved me, He set me on a journey, not of my choosing but for my good, to bring me into an **undistracted devotion** to Him.

In the pages to come, we will look at the many **distractions** or hindrances that prevent us from giving our full attention and devotion to the Lord—**distractions** like discontentment, busyness, finances, worry, anxiety, and lack of self-control.

In 1 Corinthians 7:35, Paul said, "Now I say this for your own benefit; not to restrict you, but to promote what is appropriate and secure **undistracted devotion** to the Lord" (AMP). In the prior verses, Paul's message was centered around the discussion of being single versus being married. In this verse, we see that his main message was to encourage the people to secure an **undistracted devotion** to the Lord.

Like Paul, I am praying that the words within this book and those within God's Word will encourage you to secure an **undistracted devotion** to the Lord—to seek the things of **greater importance**!

Dianne

[2]John Bloom, *Lord, Deliver Me from Distractions* (*desiringGod.org*, December 6, 2016).

Distraction

God did not create you to live a distracted life.
God created you to live a Jesus-infused life.
— Author Unknown

*W*e are living in an incredibly **busy** world. The **busyness** has become a **distraction** and is robbing many Christians of quality time with the Lord and their families. Not only is busyness a **distraction** but so are things such as self-centeredness, unforgiveness, financial strain, social media, and difficult relationships. Each of these can draw us away from choosing those things of **greater importance** in our lives, such as time with the Lord, reading our Bible, prayer, quality time with those we love, and ministering to the hurting.

> *If we allow ourselves to become preoccupied by something, it can distract us from being preoccupied with Jesus.*[3]

Our attention often gravitates to those things that are important to us. So, if you are regularly **distracted** by something, pay attention to what that is and how it is affecting your life and the lives of those around you. I read a quote as I was preparing this lesson: "A **distraction** doesn't pull you away from **your** primary goal, but it reveals your true desires." **Distractions** can often bring to light those things we love and rob us of the things that add value and spiritual depth to our lives.

Martha is a good example of this. As much as I dislike picking on Martha—for I am a lot like her—she provides a great example of one who was distracted by the **lesser things** but also of one who chose what she **loved** over what was best for her. Her choices revealed her true desires.

While Jesus was teaching in Martha's home, she was **distracted** by the work to be done in the kitchen. Noticing that her sister, Mary, was sitting at Jesus' feet, rather than helping, she complained to Him. He responded, "Martha, Martha, you are worried and **distracted** by many things; there is need of only one thing. Mary has chosen the better part, which will not be taken away from her" (Luke 10:41-42 NRSV).

Martha was **distracted** from Jesus' teaching because she was anxious about how she would feed all the people in her home without her sister's help. Serving people was her focus rather than submitting to Jesus.

What **distraction** is keeping you from fully submitting to Jesus?

Do the **distractions** you allow in your life reveal your true desires?

Martha's devotion to service and hospitality, though a good thing, robbed her of spending time with Jesus—of far **greater importance**!

> *So, then, be careful how you live. Do not be unwise but wise, making the best use of your time because the times are evil. Therefore, do not be foolish, but understand what the Lord's will is.*
> *Ephesians 5:15-17 ISV*

[3]hhps://www.heavensinspirations.com/lifes-distractions.html

Day One

When I think of the word **devotion**, I think about my husband, Mark. After he was saved, the things he devoted his life to changed drastically. Before Christ, he was devoted to money, success, and the pursuit of "things" that seemingly brought happiness and satisfaction. After Christ, his life was devoted to knowing God through His Word and prayer, loving God with all his heart, and loving people. He would often say in his testimony that before Christ he used people for his own gain, but after accepting Christ he loved people. His **devotion** to work, money, and things was completely replaced with a new, deep **devotion** to God and others.

The word *devote* (devoted, devotion) refers to applying time or oneself completely to some activity, purpose, or cause. It means having a very loyal and strong commitment to a cause or person.

1. If those closest to you were asked where your **devotion** lies, what would be their answer? Examine your heart and answer honestly below.

2. Write Luke 12:34 below.

The *things* upon which your **devotion** rests will reveal what is in your heart. Before Christ, Mark's treasures were found in success, money, and possessions. He gave his heart and **devotion** to each one.

The New Living Translation says, "Wherever your treasure is, there the desires of your heart will also be" (Luke 12:34).

3. Just for the sake of today's lesson, let's substitute the word **devotion** for the word desires.

"Wherever your treasure is, there the _____ of your heart will also be."

4. Now, considering the definition of the word devote, how does substituting the word **devotion** change the meaning of this verse for you?

I was reading about the life of Dr. David Livingstone, a missionary, physician, philanthropist, and explorer. He was from England, and he was called by God to minister in Africa in the 1800s with his wife, Mary. Dr. Livingstone was the first white man to cross Africa with the gospel of Christ. He endured hunger, disease, hardship, loneliness, dreadful fevers, pneumonia, loss, and ridicule.

A friend, Mr. Stanley, said of him, "I grant he is not an angel; but approaches to that being as near as the nature of a living man will allow. His gentleness never forsakes him; his hopefulness never deserts him. No harassing anxieties, **distraction** of mind, long separation from home and kindred, can make him complain. He thinks 'all will come out right at last;' he has such faith in the goodness of Providence."[4]

Dr. Livingstone was **devoted** to God and the calling on his life to reach the natives of Africa. Nothing would *distract* him from that call. I wonder if we could find a man (or woman) today who would be willing to endure such hardship, loneliness, and difficulty to fulfill his **devotion** to God?

When I got to the chapter of his death, I found myself tearful. You may be asking, why tears for a man you did not know and who lived so long ago? The reason is because of his **devotion**, determination, and commitment to God's call on his life. I wondered about my own **devotion** to God. I had to ask myself whether I would remain devoted even in the most horrendous circumstances, or would I be distracted and derailed from my calling?

5. In Paul Tripp's book, *A Quest for More*, he asked this question: "What is the focus of your life's energies and intentions?"[5] How would you answer this question?

Dr. Livingstone's focus was clear! His energies and intentions were focused on the faithfulness to, and the fulfillment of, God's calling upon his life. He refused to be distracted, and therefore, he accomplished incredible things for Christ that are still spoken of today.

PONDER:

Will my devotion to God, and what I have done for Him, live on for centuries after I am gone?

MEDITATE:

Now I say this for your own benefit; not to restrict you, but to promote
what is appropriate and secure undistracted devotion to the Lord.
1 Corinthians 7:35 AMP

PRAY:

God, only You know what lies in the recesses of my heart. Would You reveal those less important things in my life that draw my attention and devotion away from You? Help me set my affections on You, and You alone, with undistracted devotion.
Amen!

[4]Mrs. J.H. Worchester, Jr., *David Livingstone, The First to Cross Africa with the Gospel* (Chicago, Illinois: Moody Press, 1987). P.172
[5]Paul David Tripp, *A Quest for More* (Greensboro, North Carolina: New Growth Press, 2008). P. 131

Day Two

I can be the worst at becoming **distracted** by the less important things. I cannot tell you how many times I have needed to attend to meal preparations for company coming to dinner only to get totally **distracted** creating a centerpiece for the table. One of my greatest **distractions** comes from a small device called an iPhone. How does such a small thing wield so much power over us? How can a grown woman be so **distracted** by such a small device? Well, while it may be a small device, it is a powerful one! With one ding of a chime, our attention can be easily pulled away.

1. Write 1 Peter 5:8 below.

I recently heard a young woman speak on the things in our lives that keep us from praising God. She held up her iPhone and asked, "Have you ever noticed that the apple has a bite out of it?" She went on to say, "Satan **distracted** Eve in the garden with an apple; perhaps our iPhones are an instrument of Satan in our lives." The women in the audience laughed. But this is certainly something to think about. We must be on guard against the things that are **distractions** in our lives.

Because the enemy cannot destroy you, his job is to distract you. —Author Unknown

---

The above statement is true. If you look in the book of Job, you will see that Satan could not *utterly destroy* Job, and God will not allow him to destroy us as His children. But Satan has all the power to draw us off track.

The word **distraction** is defined as *anything that prevents someone from giving full attention to something else.*

2. What does Satan use to distract you, to keep you from giving your full attention to God?

Years ago, I drove five friends to a conference in Georgia. There was a great deal of conversation and laughter the first few hours. So much so, that as we passed through Birmingham, we missed the small 40-by-24-inch sign on the pole at the side of the interstate that said, "Atlanta Exit." Now, this was before Google Maps or Siri. When we realized that we had missed our exit, we had only one option, to stop at a gas station and ask for directions. The sweet older man drew a map that took us from one dark Alabama two-lane highway to another until we reached Atlanta—very late, I might add.

After the amazing conference, as we were preparing to head back to Memphis, our friend's husband, knowing we had gotten lost on the way, gave us directions for getting out of the city. He said, "Whatever you do, don't miss Interstate 20 west." "Got it," we responded. So, off we went. Everyone was talking, and the oxygen level in the car was no doubt at a minimum! We talked about the different seminars, the food we ate, the time with our friends who lived in the area, and a million other things. We eventually came to Interstate 20, and off we went rejoicing that we had found our way. The conversation continued, meandering from one topic to another. Shocking—I know! Before we knew it, two hours had passed. About that time, I looked ahead of us to see a large billboard that read, "Welcome to South Carolina." Oh my! We were so **distracted** with our conversation that we failed to see we had gone east on Interstate 20 instead of west!

Distractions destroy actions. If it is not moving you towards your purpose, leave it alone. —Author Unknown

---

Our **distraction** definitely destroyed our proper action—to go west. And it certainly did not move us toward our purpose of getting home that day! When you and I are not attentive and on guard, we can easily become **distracted** and not just while traveling—but in life.

3. As children of God, our purpose in life is to glorify Him. So, what **distractions** are keeping you from fulfilling your divine purpose in life?

4. Fill in the blanks from Galatians 5:18 (ICB) below.

"But if you _____ the Spirit _____ you, you are _____ under the _____."

It is the Holy Spirit who guards us against **distractions**. If our attention is focused on our divine purpose of living to glorify Christ by allowing the Holy Spirit to have control over our lives, we are less likely to be **distracted** and drawn away.

PONDER:

*Are your **distractions** keeping you from living a life in purposeful pursuit of Christ?*

MEDITATE:

Be on your guard; stand firm in the faith; be courageous; be strong. 1 Corinthians 16:13 NIV

PRAY:

Father, would You guard my mind against the distractions that are keeping me from living in purposeful pursuit of You? Help me to remain focused, attentive, and obedient to Your Spirit, glorifying You in every aspect of my life.
Amen!

Day Three

I have often wondered why we as Christians allow what others think of us to **distract** us from our pursuit of God and our obedience to Him? Early on in our journey of Mark's battle with Multiple System Atrophy, God was leading us in a direction that many people did not understand. Mark said to me, "Dianne, we have one voice and one alone we are to listen to, and that is God's voice. We have one person and one alone that we are to please, and that is God." We did not allow the voices of others to be a **distraction**. But rather, we attuned our hearts and ears to God, obeying what we felt He was asking of us, whether others understood it or not.

> *Don't let the noise of the world **distract** you from hearing the voice of God. —Author Unknown*

A great example of a man who was able to tune out the **distractions** caused by the voices of others and attune his heart and ears to God, obeying what God was asking of him, was Noah.

Read Genesis 6:5-22.

1. What did you learn about Noah in verses 8-10?

2. What did God ask Noah to do? Why?

Now, think about this. Noah had never seen rain, a boat, nor a flood. The ark God asked him to build was 450 feet long, 75 feet wide, and 45 feet high. The inside capacity would have been 1.4 million cubic feet with an approximate total deck area of 95,700 square feet. There were no architects for him to consult and no blueprints to go by. According to Ken Ham's *Answers in Genesis* website, it took Noah approximately 55 to 75 years to build the ark. Now, that is *devotion*!

Not only had Noah never seen rain, a boat , nor a flood, but neither had the people of his day.

Can you imagine the ridicule Noah endured for 55 to 75 years as he attempted to express his **devotion** to God through obeying what He asked of him in building an ark?

3. Has there ever been a time in your life when God was asking something of you and you were **distracted** by the voices of others? Explain.

4. Read John 10:1-16. What do verses 4, 14, and 16 tell you about the sheep's relationship to the Shepherd?

Sheep listen and obey the Shepherd because He knows what is best for them; they can trust Him. Noah remained devoted and was not **distracted** by the comments and ridicule of others.

5. What was the outward sign of Noah's devotion to God? (Hint: fill in the letters below.)

O__E__I__N__E

Noah was obedient to God, his calling, and the work God gave him to do. He was not **distracted**. He stayed **devoted** to the things of **greater importance** and ignored those of **lesser importance**. He listened to God's voice and not the voices of others.

> *You can't do big things if you're distracted by little things. —Author Unknown*

6. How would you apply the above statement to Noah's life? To your life?

PONDER:

*Are you letting the noise of the world **distract** you from hearing the voice of God?*

MEDITATE:

*But this command I gave them: Obey my voice, and I will be your God,
and you shall be my people. And walk in all the way that I command you,
that it may be well with you. Jeremiah 7:23 ESV*

PRAY:

*Oh, Father, I am so sorry that I have allowed the voices of others to be
a distraction in my life. Their loud shouts often drown out Your voice.
Help me to have a spirit that obeys, a heart that desires to please You above
all else and all others, and ears that are attuned to Your voice.
Amen!*

Day Four

When I was five, we were living in Kansas City, Missouri, while my dad was earning a seminary degree. With my dad in school, and my mom earning her education as well, our family of five lived very meagerly. The house we lived in was very small. Not only did we three kids share one bedroom, but we shared one bike!

Obviously, with one bike only one person could ride it at a time. Well, not necessarily! One day, my sister said she had figured out a way that we could both ride the bike at the same time. She convinced me to climb up on the handlebars with my feet resting on the front fender. Wanting to ride, I chose to do just that. I positioned myself securely on the handlebars, holding on tightly as I planted my feet, one on top of the other, on the fender. Off we went. It was really fun until we topped the hill and headed down. The bike began to pick up speed, and as it did, my sister began to lose control. The front tire bumped against the curb, and the bike began to wobble back and forth until she lost complete control. Off I went, flying across the pavement face-first. She fell to the pavement, and within seconds we were both bleeding and crying as we ran into the house.

Life is filled with choices. I made the choice that day to be **distracted** from what I knew was the right thing and to listen to my sister. When it comes to **distraction** or **devotion**, we have a choice.

In this week's lesson, we have seen examples of this in God's story.

1. Reflecting on Day 3, did Noah choose **distraction** or **devotion**? What difference did his choice make in his life and the lives of his family members?

2. Reflecting on the Week 1 Introduction, did Mary choose **distraction** or **devotion**? What difference did her choice make in her life and the lives of those around her?

In Deuteronomy 30:19-20, Moses said to the children of Israel, "Today I have given you the choice between life and death, between blessings and curses. Now I call on heaven and earth to witness the choice you make. Oh, that you would choose life, so that you and your descendants might live! You can make this choice by loving the Lord your God, obeying him, and committing yourself firmly to him. This is the key to your life. And if you love and obey the Lord, you will live long in the land the Lord swore to give your ancestors Abraham, Isaac, and Jacob" (NLT).

> *It takes deliberate pursuit and attentiveness to grow closer to God.*

In Deuteronomy, Moses was saying to the people of Israel, avoid **distractions**, pursue **devotion** to God, be attentive, obey Him, and in doing so, you will live!

3. In your own life, what have been the consequences of choosing **distraction** over pursuing **devotion**?

4. In what ways can you be more deliberate in your pursuit and attentiveness to Christ?

5. In Hebrews 2:1 (ESV), what warning did Paul give us?

Distractions can be destructive. We must deliberately and attentively pursue truth, lest we drift away.

PONDER:

It takes deliberate pursuit and attentiveness to grow closer to God [6]
—John Bloom

MEDITATE:

*Enter by the narrow gate. For the gate is wide and the way is easy that leads
to destruction, and those who enter by it are many. For the gate is narrow and the way
is hard that leads to life, and those who find it are few. Matthew 7:13-14 ESV*

PRAY:

*Lord, I know the distractions I choose can bring destruction to me spiritually.
It is a daily choice. I can choose life (devotion) or death (distraction). Help me to guard
my heart and mind against distractions and to choose a life of full pursuit in devotion to You.
Amen!*

[6]John Bloom, *Lord, Deliver Me from Distractions* (*desiringGod.org*, December 6, 2016).

Day Five

After Mark's diagnosis and our home was sold, turning us into nomads, I had a crisis of **devotion** to the Lord. I wanted to run and avoid the pain of what was to come. I had a choice to make: Would I remain **devoted** to God? I will be very honest with you—I struggled. Please understand, I loved God, but the circumstances I found myself in caused me to struggle with the question of my **devotion** to Him and His love for me. I wrestled with surrendering to what God was asking of me. Could I remain **devoted** to Him? Could I trust Him?

Devotion to God is still a voluntary thing; hence the differences of attainment among Christians.[7]
—Hudson Taylor

---

1. The word **voluntary** means *done or acting of one's own free will.* In light of this, what do you think Hudson Taylor meant by the quote above?

We can either voluntarily choose **devotion** to God or choose **distraction**. If we choose **distraction**, there are consequences; we saw this in Martha's life. But if we choose **devotion**, there are blessings; we saw this in Noah's life. Each of these had a choice, as did I. God was patient with me, as He is with each of His children. I came to a place of surrendering my will to God's will and choosing **devotion** to Him. Upon that decision, I received many unexpected blessings.

2. Fill in the missing words of the verse in Ecclesiastes 10:2: "A wise person _____ the right road; a _____ takes the wrong one" (NLT).

We make the decision to voluntarily choose **devotion** to God, which develops godly character, or to voluntarily choose **distraction**. If we are wise, we will choose **devotion**.

Godly character flows out of devotion to God and practically confirms the reality of that devotion.[8]
—Jerry Bridges

---

[7]Hudson Taylor, https://www.azquotes.com/Hudson Taylor quotes/1311105
[8]www.searching4Christ.com/S.D.Wonenebergquotes

I am grateful for God's goodness and blessings that have come as a result of a passionate determination throughout the years of Mark's illness and, since his death, to remain **devoted** to the Lord. Let me share a few of those blessings ...

- I received joy and peace in the midst of heartache and pain.

- Through His refining work in my life, I became more like Him.

- I have developed patience as I have learned to wait on Him and trust Him in all things.

- I have developed self-control, not allowing **distractions** to draw me away from my devotion to God. As John Bloom said, "We strengthen self-control through resistance."[9]

- Because of the way in which God chose to write my story, I know Him intimately.

- I know Him as my Jehovah Jireh.

> *The fruit of patience in all its aspects—long-suffering, forbearance, endurance,*
> *and perseverance, is a fruit that is most intimately associated with our devotion to God.*
> *All character traits of godliness grow out of and have their foundation in our devotion to God,*
> *but the fruit of patience must grow out of that relationship in a particular way.[10]*
> *—Jerry Bridges*

3. List below the blessings you have received through choosing **devotion** over **distraction**.

4. What does Proverbs 13:21 tell us about God's blessings?

[9] John Bloom, *Lord, Deliver Me from Distractions* (*desiringGod.org*, December 6, 2016).
[10] Jerry Bridges, *The Practice of Godliness*, (Colorado Springs, Colorado: Nav Press, 1983.) P. 217.

PONDER:

Lord, help me, for I am often lukewarm and chill; unbelief mars my confidence, sin makes me forget Thee. Let the weeds that grow in my soul be cut at their roots; grant me to know that I truly live only when I live to Thee, that all else is trifling.[11]

MEDITATE:

And this is God's plan: Both Gentiles and Jews who believe the Good News share equally in the riches inherited by God's children. Both are part of the same body, and both enjoy the promise of blessings because they belong to Christ Jesus.
Ephesians 3:6 NLT

PRAY:

Father, I pray that my life would be a picture of devotion to You and You alone. Thank You for the blessings You have bestowed upon my life. Help me to be faithful in resisting the pull of distraction in seeking to build godly character in every aspect of my life.
Amen!

[11]https://www.goodreads.com/work/quotes/26869697-puritan-prayers-devotions

Week One Menu

Mango Salsa Chicken

4 boneless chicken breasts, (1 to 2 inches thick)

Seasoning salt

Pepper to taste

½ cup vinaigrette dressing for marinade (your choice)

Place chicken breasts in a zipper-lock bag, seal, and tenderize with meat mallet. Remove to new zipper-lock bag and cover in dressing to marinate. Seal bag and chill at least 2 to 4 hours before grilling. Place on grill and cook for 5 to 6 minutes on each side. Remove and top with salsa. Note: For grilling, cooking time will vary based on thickness of chicken breast and temperature of grill. To bake in oven, place chicken in 9x13 inch casserole dish and bake for 30 minutes at 350°F.

Salsa

2 tablespoons balsamic vinegar

1 teaspoon garlic, minced

1 tablespoon Italian seasoning (Optional)

2 mangoes, peeled and diced

1 avocado, peeled and cubed

Mix balsamic vinegar, garlic and Italian seasonings. Chill for 30 minutes. Add mango and avocado. Toss to coat. Note: Vinaigrette dressing can either be a recipe from scratch or store-bought.

Black Rice

1 cup black rice

2 cups chicken broth

1½ teaspoons garlic, minced

¼ cup butter

1½ teaspoons onion powder

1 tablespoon Italian seasoning

1 teaspoon salt

½ teaspoon pepper

Place chicken broth in large saucepan over medium-high heat; add butter, garlic, and seasonings. Cook until butter is melted and broth comes to a boil. Add rice, cover, and reduce heat to simmer. Cook for 30-35 minutes. Turn off heat; remain covered for an additional 10 minute. Serve warm.

Oven Roasted Green Beans

1 (16 ounce) bag frozen green beans

4 tablespoons olive oil

Salt and pepper to taste

1 tablespoon garlic powder

½ tablespoon onion powder

½ cup Parmesan cheese, grated

Pre-heat oven to 375°F. Place green beans in gallon size zipper-lock bag. Pour oil over beans. Sprinkle salt and pepper, garlic powder, and onion powder over beans. Seal bag; shake to cover thoroughly with oil and seasonings. Place on baking sheet pan and bake for 20 to 25 minutes, tossing once with metal spatula. Remove from oven and top with grated Parmesan cheese. Turn oven off and place baking sheet back in oven until cheese is melted. Serve. Optional: Substitute 4 cups fresh green beans for frozen. Cooking time may vary.

Brownie Cheesecake Trifle

GHIRARDELLI DOUBLE CHOCOLATE BROWNIES:
Prepare box according to instructions.

CREAM CHEESE FILLING:

1 (8 ounce) cream cheese, room temperature

1 cup peanut butter, smooth or crunchy

1 cup powdered sugar

2 to 3 tablespoons milk

In mixing bowl at medium-high speed, beat cream cheese until smooth and light. Add peanut butter, mix until incorporated. On low speed, mix in powdered sugar and 2 tablespoons of milk until fluffy. Note: If too stiff for spreading, add additional tablespoon of milk one at a time until desired thickness. Set aside.

WHIPPED CREAM:

1½ cups heavy whipping cream

½ cup powdered sugar

1½ teaspoons vanilla

With mixer, beat whipping cream until it begins to thicken. Add powdered sugar and vanilla. Continue mixing until mixture is light and fluffy. Note: Use small, frozen tub thawed whipped topping as an alternative.

CANDY:
Any variety.

Reece's Peanut Butter cups, chopped

Heath bar pieces (baking section of grocery)

Hershey Milk Chocolate bars, chopped

1 (16.5 ounce) Torani caramel sauce

In a trifle bowl, layer ⅓ brownies, ½ cream cheese filling, caramel sauce (thin layer), ⅓ candy pieces (thin layer). Repeat. Top with whipped cream. Note: If desired, garnish with reserved brownie chunks, candy, and then drizzle with caramel. Chill well, preferably overnight, before serving.

SHORT-CUTS...

- **MANGO SALSA CHICKEN:** Chicken can be tenderized, seasoned, and placed in marinade inside a zipper-lock bag and refrigerated up to 24 hours in advance.

- **HOMEMADE VINAIGRETTE DRESSING:** For extra smooth homemade Vinaigrette dressing: Combine the ingredients and an ice cube in a screw-top jar and shake vigorously. Discard the ice cube once the dressing is mixed.

- **SALSA:** Once cut, the mango and avocado will turn colors. Prepare and refrigerate salsa no earlier than 30 minutes prior to serving.

- **CUTTING A MANGO:** Hold the mango on its side and cut down on either side of the central seed. You will end with two big halves plus the central seed. Place each half on the cutting board with peel facing down and cut the exposed flesh in a horizontal and vertical pattern, taking care not to cut deep through skin. Then invert the whole half to push out the cubes. Eat cubes from skin or remove with a sharp knife.

- **CUTTING AVOCADO:** Grip the avocado gently on one side with one hand. With a large, sharp knife in the other hand, cut the avocado lengthwise around the seed. Open the two halves to expose the pit. Remove the pit by using a tablespoon to scoop out. At this point, you can either scoop out the avocado flesh with a spoon for making guacamole, or slice the avocado into segments. To make it easier to scoop out the avocado flesh, take a small dinner knife and gently make cuts in the avocado flesh in a cross-hatch pattern, careful not to break through the avocado peel. Then use a spoon to easily scoop out the avocado pieces.

- **BLACK RICE** can be cooked in the morning and re-heated prior to serving dinner.

- **ROASTED GREEN BEANS:** Place green beans in bag earlier in the day with oil and seasonings (minus cheese) then refrigerate.

- **BROWNIE CHEESECAKE TRIFLE:** Brownies can be baked a day or two ahead and frozen. Filling and whipping cream can be made the morning prior to serving. Trifle can be assembled up to two hours ahead.

HEALTHY TIPS...

- **MANGO SALSA CHICKEN:** Use Organic Chicken breasts.

- **VINAIGRETTE DRESSING:** Make your own vinaigrette dressing to avoid additives and preservatives.

- **SALSA:** Health benefits of Mangoes: Mango has been proven to help in preventing cancer due to its high antioxidant compounds. It can also aid in lowering cholesterol due to its high levels of fiber, pectin, and vitamin C. Many use it externally as a way to clear the skin. It has been proven to help with eye health due to the high levels of Vitamin A, with just 1 cup providing 25% of the needed daily value. This delicious fruit improves the digestive system and boosts the immune system. It is high in vitamin C and E.

- **SALSA:** Choose mangoes with unblemished, yellowish blushed with red skin. Ripe mangoes will yield to gentle pressure and have a sweet tropical fragrance. Avoid any with shriveled or black-speckled skin. To ripen green rock-hard mangoes, place in a paper bag on kitchen counter overnight. Check the mangoes for ripeness every one or two days. If the fruit re,ains firm but indents slightly under pressure, it is ripe. Mangoes usually take between three to eight days to ripen.

- **SALSA:** Health benefits of Avocado: Avocados are considered one of the healthiest foods on the planet, containing many nutrients and vitamins such as A, B, C, and K. They are rich in folic acid and are proven to help maintain a healthy heart. Due to the level of potassium, they aid in lowering blood pressure and cholesterol. They help as an anti-inflammatory, and aid in regulating blood sugar levels and reducing strokes.

- **SALSA:** Avocados ripen best off the tree, so you'll find that a lot of them are unripe when you shop. Look for avocados that feel heavy. The skin should be dark, with a hint of green, and taut, with no dents.

- **BLACK RICE:** This is a fun rice that not very many people have tried. It is incredibly healthy. The bran hull of black rice contains one of the highest levels of anthocyanins found in food. The grain has a similar amount of fiber to brown rice and, like brown rice, has a mild, nutty taste. Note: Brown rice may be substituted in the recipe.

- **BROWNIE CHEESECAKE TRIFLE:** Our healthy tip for this dessert is *do not eat it*—if you are trying to be healthy. But, if you just want to enjoy life—*eat* it! A dessert every once in a while will not hurt you!

Contentment

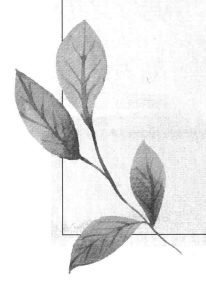

And when you learn the secret of contentment,
you will see God in a new way.
— Linda Dillow

Contentment Introduction

Several years ago, Mark's company transferred our family to Boston, Massachusetts, for the second time. We had lived there just five years prior, but the difference the second time was where we were spiritually. The first time we were on a fast track to success, and we were not saved. The second time we were born again believers leaving our Christian friends behind in Texas. I can remember joking with Mark about the words spoken by Paul in Philippians, "Not that I speak in respect of want: for I have learned, in *whatsoever state* I am, therewith to be content" (Philippians 4:11 NAS). I noted that obviously Paul had never lived in the state of Massachusetts, especially during the wintertime! Not to offend any Bostonians, but I am a Southern girl! We laughed, knowing that Paul was in no way talking of a specific state, but rather a condition (state) of the heart. At the time, when it came to the (condition) state of my heart, I was content only as long as the paycheck was coming in, and I could get whatever I wanted when I wanted it.

In Linda Dillow's book, *Calm My Anxious Heart*, she says, "God can rid your heart of greed, but it's your responsibility to remove yourself from situations that promote greediness."[12] I was continually placing myself in situations of feeding the greed monster. I felt obligated to purchase items from any store from which I received a coupon. After all, they were kind enough to send it to me! Right? I was always looking at new construction, reminding me that my house was becoming outdated by the day! I found myself dissatisfied with my home. I was greedy, and I did not even recognize it.

In the first years of Mark's illness, God began stripping away everything I deemed important in my life—a job, an income, our home, and Mark's health. God's stripping away of all I deemed important was a painful process. But eventually, each of my losses led me to a greater understanding of true **contentment**.

After our home sold, we moved five times in five and a half years. With each move we stored more things and used less; our friends tried to talk me into getting rid of many of our things, but I was not ready. I was still holding on to *my* stuff! After five years, God provided a home for us that was equipped with the special handicap features Mark needed. After we moved in, I hosted a dinner. As I walked our guests through the house telling of the miraculous ways in which God had provided, I began to tear up. At that moment, in sharing with them God's blessings and goodness, I suddenly realized that He had brought me to a place of true **contentment**! I am very grateful for my home, but it no longer defines me! I am content with or without it. If God ever chooses to take it away, I will remain grateful!

> *Contentment is a state of the heart, not a state of affairs.*[13] —Linda Dillow

God changed the state of my affairs, but deeper than that, He changed the state of my heart!

Due to my greed and discontentment, I wasted so much of our hard earned money over the years. I regret that, but I am thankful that I serve a God of grace and mercy! He took me to a place I would never have chosen, stripping away all my *stuff* in order to show me the secret of true **contentment**—Him! To God be all glory and praise!

[12]Linda Dillow, *Calm My Anxious Heart* (Colorado Springs, Colorado: Nav Press, 2007). P. 97
[13]Linda Dillow, *Calm My Anxious Heart* (Colorado Springs, Colorado: Nav Press, 2007). P. 13

CONTENT OR DISCONTENT?

Answer the following questions with a Y for Yes or N for No. Score the number of N's you marked. See Chart below.

____Have you complained to anyone about your income this month?

____Have you bought anything on credit that you won't be able to pay for when the bill comes in?

____Is there anything you want to change about the way you look?

____Are you inwardly jealous when someone you know purchases something you cannot afford?

____Do you often dream of having things you never expect to be able to get?

____Have you complained about your car this week?

____Have you complained about your clothes this week?

____Have you complained about the weather this week?

____Do you think that you could be happy if you just had a little more income or material things?

____Do you worry about who will take care of your physical needs?

____Do you fear that in surrendering to God, He might send you somewhere you don't want to go?

____Do you fall apart emotionally when something of value or a treasured possession gets broken?

My total:_____

Key…

Give yourself one point for each question that you could honestly answer with a No.

1-6 points – You are very discontent and probably unhappy

7-9 points – You have much to learn about contentment

10-11 points – You are fairly content but God has more for you

12 points– What you have, you have by the grace of God; do not be proud

Day One

Several years ago, we rented a home on a very busy road. This thoroughfare was a connector between the north and south parts of the city and led right to the door of one of the main hospitals in town. It was the day before Christmas, and the weather was typical for that time of year. It was a rainy, dreary cold day. I was busy in the house wrapping presents when I heard an incredible crashing sound. I ran to the front door, looked out into the street and saw nothing. But as I glanced to my left, there was a car right up against the porch covered in shreds of holly branches and leaves. I quickly opened the door to hear a voice calling for help. The young woman inside had lost control of her car on the wet pavement. As she rounded the curve, her car went barreling through our neighbor's yard, across our driveway, and along the front of our home. The house was over thirty years old; therefore the hedges were mature and the row of holly bushes lining the long front porch were deeply rooted. The policeman told us that if it had not been for the row of deeply rooted hedges, the car would have come right through the living room. The deeply-rooted hedges protected us from being harmed. Often, as Christians, our **spiritual hedge** is not deeply rooted, and therefore we are unprotected against Satan's lies—those darts (thoughts) he places in our minds to cause us to be **discontented**.

1. We, as women, struggle with **contentment** in many areas of our lives. What are some of the areas where you personally struggle?

Read Matthew 4:1-11.

2. What "weapon" did Jesus use in response to Satan's lies?

The opposite of a lie is truth.

> *Jesus was able to resist all of the devil's temptations because he not only knew Scripture, but he also obeyed it.*[14]
> NLT Parallel Study Bible

[14]NLT *Parallel Study Bible* (Carol Stream, Illinois: Tyndale House Publishing, 2011). P. 1741

3. What does Ephesians 6:17 say about God's Word and how we can use it against Satan's lies?

4. What can we do to deepen our **spiritual** root system in order to fight off the lies of Satan that cause **discontentment**?

Paul says, "We demolish arguments and every high-minded thing that is raised up against the knowledge of God, taking every thought captive to obey Christ" (2 Corinthians 10:4-5 HCSB).

5. How do we go about taking every thought captive?

Listening to the enemy's lies and falling prey to his desire for us to continually compare ourselves to others causes anxiety in the heart and life of a believer. Comparison is a tool of the enemy to bring about **discontentment**. Many young women today are struggling with anxiety and depression because they continually compare themselves with others.

- An article in a women's magazine stated. "Anxiety disorders are the most common and pervasive mental disorders in the United States. An estimated 264 million people worldwide have an anxiety disorder. Women are nearly twice as likely as men to be diagnosed with an anxiety disorder."[15]

- Another article from pschycentral.com said, "Recent research has shown that using social networking sites, namely Facebook, can increase people's stress levels, produce anxiety and negatively affect a person's sense of self."[16]

6. What are some major **technology** resources Satan uses to cause you to compare yourself to others?

[15]Article: *Women and Anxiety*, https://adaa.org/find-help-for/women/anxiety

[16]Marissa Maldonado, *The Anxiety of Facebook* (https://psychcentral.com/lib/the-anxiety-of-facebook, October 8, 2018).

If spending time on Facebook, Pinterest, Twitter, or Instagram is the source of a constant comparison of your life to others, get off and stay off! Consider taking a fast from social media. You might just find that you are much more **content** with who you are and what you have.

Romans 12:2 says, "Let God transform you into a new person by changing the way you think" (NLT). We renew our minds when we take negative thoughts captive and allow God to transform our minds. Pray and ask God to help you **fix** your mind on what is good, pure, and true. When you set your mind on God's Word and His good gifts, and being spiritually rooted, it leads to **contentment** and a heart of peace.

PONDER:

*All of us desperately need **contentment**, a state of inner peace separate from our circumstances.*
*Ultimately, **contentment** is more a shift in attitude than a change in circumstances.[17]*
—Linda Dillow

MEDITATE:

Yet true godliness with contentment is itself great gain.
1 Timothy 6:6 NLT

PRAY:

Father, my mind is often open to the lies of the enemy; I fail to guard it with the truth of Your Word.
Lord, help me to be deeply rooted in Your Word. Transform me into the person You desire me to be
by changing the way I think. Help me to resist the enemy's temptation to compare myself with others,
thus leading me to be discontent. I desire to be content with every aspect of my life, knowing
that You provide all that I need, and that within a heart of contentment lies peace.
Amen!

[17]Linda Dillow, *Calm My Anxious Heart* (Colorado Springs, Colorado: Nav Press, 2007). P. 35

Day Two

I have four granddaughters, ranging in ages. They are all uniquely different, each having her own personality, body shape, hair color, eye color, and temperament. But, I have found one thing they have in common; those that have reached puberty, each struggled with their body type. They were self-conscious of their early development and the tummy that came along with that particular season of a young lady's life. I tried to encourage them to not be so hard on themselves because their bodies still had a lot of changing to go through; that tummy just might decide to settle somewhere else—as we as grown women know!

As a pre-teen, I remember the feelings I had about my looks. I saw myself as a large boned girl with huge thighs and hips. A few years ago, I found it funny, and somewhat sad, when I pulled out pictures of myself as a teen and realized that I actually looked pretty good. It was funny in that I had a nicer shape than I thought and sad because I wasted time and energy focusing on the outer person instead of the inner person. My thoughts and the image I had of myself were not true. Satan had deceived me!

In yesterday's lesson, we came to understand that the source of much of our **discontentment** begins in our thought life.

- It is vital as Christian women that we be on guard against Satan's schemes to defeat, discourage, and destroy us.

- We must "take every thought captive."

- We must be deeply rooted in God's Word, strengthening our **spiritual hedge** in order to ward off Satan's lies.

In the days to come, we will discover the key areas in which women can be vulnerable, thus leading them to be **discontented**. Today, we will be looking at the topic of self-image—the way we see ourselves versus the way God sees us.

Nancy DeMoss Wolgemuth in *Lies Women Believe*, says, "What we believe about God is crucial because it affects what we believe about everything else. One of the areas that is particularly impacted by our view of God is our view of ourselves."[18]

1. Do you believe this statement to be true? Is the way you view God reflected in the way you view yourself? Explain.

David says about God our Creator, "For it was You who created my inward parts; You knit me together in my mother's womb. I will praise You because I have been remarkably and wonderfully made" (Psalm 139:13-14a HCSB).

 [18]Nancy DeMoss Wolgemuth, *Lies Women Believe* (Chicago, Illinois: Moody Publishers, 2001). P. 64

2. Satan will lie to us about ourselves causing us to be **discontented** with the way we look. God never lies. When He says we were created "remarkably and wonderfully," He means it! List below some of the truths you know about yourself based on who God is and what His Word says, then write the lie Satan has used to cause you to doubt God.

TRUTH: LIE:

Nancy goes on to say, "If we have believed lies about God we will believe lies about ourselves, lies such as physical beauty matters more than inner beauty. What we believe about ourselves determines how we live. We as Christian women should seek to reflect the beauty, order, excellence, and grace of God through both our outward and inner person."[19]

3. What does 1 Samuel 16:7 tell us about the way God sees us in contrast to the way man sees us?

If the lie we believe is that outer beauty matters more than inner beauty, then we will act on that lie, spending a lifetime to gain something that is quickly fading away!

Charm is deceptive, and beauty does not last; but a woman who fears the Lord will be greatly praised.
Proverbs 31:30 NLT

The *NLT Parallel Study Bible* says of Proverbs 31:30, "A woman's character is more important than her physical beauty."[20]

I belong to a small gym and on every wall of this gym are mirrors—the enemy of every woman! To some degree, I am kidding. But, mirrors can be our friend or our foe. I have found that some mirrors lie, but there are others that are brutally honest. My bathroom mirror lies to me. Now, what I mean by that is that, no matter what I put on, it looks good in that mirror. I always look thin and attractive.

[19]Nancy DeMoss Wolgemuth, *Lies Women Believe* (Chicago, Illinois: Moody Publishers, 2001). P.65, 67, 80
[20]*NLT Parallel Study Bible* (Carol Stream, Illinois: Tyndale House Publishing, 2011). P. 1137

Clothing stores should place my bathroom mirror in every dressing room! What great sales they would have. On the other hand, my gym mirrors are brutally honest, revealing areas that need improving. Often, other women become like my gym mirrors. In them, we see all our "areas" that need improving. Before we know it, there isn't one thing we like about ourselves or our lives. We see all that is wrong with us. We look at other women and compare ourselves, falling short every time!

> *It's probably no news to anyone that many women, instead of thanking God for the frame He's given them, spend their time trying to change it.*[21] —*Linda Dillow*

4. So, if Linda's statement is true, how do we as godly women come to the place of being **content** with whom God made us to be—tummies, thighs, hips, and all?

Realizing that we are vulnerable to the enemy and his efforts to direct our focus on our outward appearance, we must take "every thought captive" and replace it with the truth of His Word. This will change us from the inside out into the beautiful radiant creations God intends for us to be!

5. When we take a look into God's spiritual mirror, His Word, the truth of who we are is revealed. What does 1 Peter 3:3-5 (The Living Bible) say about having a Christ-like beauty?

[21]Linda Dillow, *Calm My Anxious Heart* (Colorado Springs, Colorado: Nav Press, 2007). P.47

PONDER:

*You will never really enjoy other people, you will never have stable emotions,
you will never lead a life of godly **contentment**, you will never conquer jealousy
and love others as you should until you thank God for making you the way He did.*[22]
—Reverend James Hufstetler

MEDITATE:

Those who look to Him are radiant, and their faces shall never be ashamed.
Psalm 34:5 ESV

PRAY:

*Father, I know intellectually that I am remarkably and wonderfully made, but often my heart
is unbelieving and my mind a literal mine field for the enemy. May I not focus my time and
energy on seeking after physical beauty and neglect the inner beauty that is so important to You.
Help me to guard my mind and set my heart on reflecting You, my Creator. Give me the desire
to please You above all else. Create in me a clean heart, O God, and make me a sweet fragrance
in the lives of others and a beautiful picture of Your love to the world.*
Amen!

[22]James Hufstetler, *"On Knowing Oneself"* (*The Banner of Truth 280*, January 1987). P. 13

Day Three

IN DAY ONE:

- We listed some of the areas in which we as women personally struggle with **contentment**.

- Take a minute and look back over your list.

- Ask God to show you in which of these areas you continue to struggle and don't allow Him total control. List them below.

Spend a few minutes praying through your list before starting today's lesson. The Bible says. "If we confess our sins, he is faithful and just to forgive us our sins" (1 John 1:9 ESV).

IN DAY TWO:

- We looked at how we as women struggle with being **contented** in the way we look.

TODAY:

- We are going to see what God says about being **contented** with what we have—our stuff!

If there is one thing that can keep us from **contentment**, other than the pull of the world, it is greed.

So, what is greed? Greed is *an intense selfish desire for something, and typically something someone else possesses*—well that last part is actually defined as jealousy. But they are closely linked!

The Study Bible for Women says of greed, "Greed is a self-centered desire for wealth and possessions. Greed generally escalates as a person acquires more possessions"[23] (HCSB).

John D. Rockefeller, a multimillionaire, was asked by a reporter, "How much money is enough money?" He replied, "Just a little more."[24] Have you ever noticed that greed is no respecter of persons; we are all prone to deal with it, the poor and even the wealthy.

Greed is a barrier to **contentment**.

Possessing a spirit of always "wanting more" will cause you to be in a continual cycle of **discontentment**. No amount of possessions will ever be good enough.

1. Fill in the blanks of the following scripture: "Then he said, "_____! Guard against every kind of _____. Life is not measured by how much you _____" (Luke 12:15 NLT).

[23]*The Study Bible for Women* HCSB (Nashville, Tennessee: Holman Bible Publishers, 2014). P. 1349
[24]John D. Rockefeller, https://starwinar.wordpress.com/daily-short-story/just-a-little-bit-more

I love the *New Life Version*. It says, "Then Jesus said to them all, "Watch yourselves! Keep from wanting all kinds of things you should not have. A man's life is not made up of things, even if he has many riches" (Luke 12:15).

Jesus warns them, "Watch yourselves! Keep from wanting." And then He tells them what makes a true man or woman is not their possessions, IRA, or their bank account—but who they are in Him.

He says, "Be on guard from all covetousness, for one's life does not consist in the abundance of his possessions" (ESV).

Let's look at a few synonyms for the word covetous: grasping, greedy, insatiable, desirous, possessive, jealous, envious, begrudging, and grabby.

2. Are these words positive or negative?

3. Are these words honoring or dishonoring to the Lord? In what ways?

They are pretty negative words. I certainly would not want anyone using any of these as an adjective to describe me!

4. Read Luke 12:16-21. Jesus follows the warning above with the story of a rich man. What words would you use to describe this man? What word does Jesus use?

5. What is the warning to us in this story?

Read Luke 12:22-31

It is really interesting to me that:

- Jesus first warns them about greed and covetousness in verse 15.

- Then in verses 16-21, He gives an example of a man who was greedy and chose to protect his possessions rather than his heart.

- Now, in verses 22-34, He tells them to not be anxious or worried about their lives. He tells them that it is His responsibility to care for His sheep as the Great Shepherd.

- He ends with these powerful words: "For where your treasure is, there will your heart be also."

Contrary to what John D. Rockefeller said, "a little bit more" or a spirit of greed will not bring peace, joy, or contentment. Greed and the desire or need for "a little bit more" will only lead to a life of **discontentment**, anxiety, self-centeredness, and constant emotional turmoil.

6. Write the definition of the word **contentment**.

7. List a few synonyms for **contentment**.

Now, look back at the definition for greed and its list of synonyms. Compare those with the definition of **contentment** and its synonyms.

8. How do you want to be defined, as a greedy woman or a **contented** woman? Explain why.

The key to **contentment** lies within the heart of every woman. If your heart is set on your earthly treasures or the earthly treasures of others, it cannot therefore be set on Christ.

9. The Bible tells us that we are not to store up our treasures on earth but in heaven.

- How does this truth change the way you look at your earthly treasures?

- What are a few examples of heavenly treasures?

The Bible tells us that our earthly treasures will pass away, they will burn up in the end. But, our heavenly treasures, the people and lives we have invested in, will live on forever. So, which is most important to you—earthly treasures or heavenly treasures? Which one should dominate your thoughts and life?

PONDER:

Gratitude turns what we have into enough.[25]
—Melody Beattie

MEDITATE:

For where your treasure is, there your heart will be also.
Luke 12:43 ESV

PRAY:

Father, I am often controlled by my wants, desires, greed, and the lure of things
that promise to satisfy, but never do. Help me to allow Your Spirit to have control
over my wants and desires; I long to be content with what I have. Remove the spirit of
greed from my heart. Help me to store up heavenly treasures that can never be taken away.
Lord, I want to find my satisfaction in You and You alone!
Amen!

[25]Melody Beattie, BrainyQuote.com, Xplore Inc, 2015.

Day Four

After riding in the back of an old pickup truck in sleet and freezing temperatures, Arthur and Wilda Mathews along with their baby Lilah, arrived in northern China for a new missionary assignment. With great anticipation and excitement, they looked forward to seeing how God was going to use them among the Mongols.

The Communist party had taken over China. At a time when many missionaries were evacuating the country, the Chinese government had extended an invitation to the Mathews to work among the Mongol people. They were honored at the request, yet, a little hesitant as to what they were getting into.

As I read their story, set in the 1950's, I was amazed at the persecution and hardships they endured. In some ways, I related to their struggle to continually trust God to give them what they needed. Please let me say, I have never sacrificed or suffered the way the Mathews did over their years of their service in China. But, I have been through an extended period of having no income, no home of my own, wondering where the monies would come from for the groceries, and the funds to pay for the health insurance. However, my life has never been threatened, I have never had to sleep in a room with no heat in the middle of a China winter, and I have never been close to starving—all experiences they endured.

1. Read 1 Timothy 6:6-8 (ESV recommended). Fill in the following blanks: "But godliness with _____ is great gain, for we brought _____ into the world, and we cannot take _____ out of the world. But if we have food and clothing, with these we will be _____."

The Mathew's desire was not for "much," they learned to be **content** and grateful for little. Their little meant just food and clothing, and not new clothing, but hand-me-downs.

Modern day Americans are not conditioned to be **content** with "little." When I think of Americans, I think of the words **abundance** or **excess**. We have an abundance of things, and we do everything in excess, yet we are **discontented** people.

2. Write the definition of the word **little**.

Synonyms for little: hardly any, slight, small, modest, minimal, insufficient, and inadequate.

3. How would you define the word **abundance**?

Synonyms for **abundance**: prosperity, affluence, opulence, luxury, plentifulness, and comfort.

Since we are women, let's use our closets as a test of little or abundant (much). This is going to be painful I know, but bear with me. If I walked into your closet, according to the definitions studied, would I say you have little or an abundance of clothing? ___Little ___Abundance

One fall, due to some home repairs, I removed my summer and spring clothing from my bedroom closet in early October, but I wanted to wait to move all my winter clothing down until after the work was completed. Well, come mid-January, my winter clothing was still upstairs. Due to that, most of the rods in my closet were sparse. I did retrieve two pairs of boots from upstairs, but other than that, I just ended up wearing what was in my closet at the time of the repairs.

- Guess what I have discovered?

- I was **content** with little.

- Having less in my closet made my decisions about what to wear a lot less complicated and stressful.

- You would think that I would have been more stressed because I had little to choose from—but not so!

> *You say, 'If I had a little more, I should be very satisfied.' You make a mistake.*
> *If you are not content with what you have, you would not be satisfied if it were doubled.*[26]
> *—Charles Spurgeon*

4. Let's replace the word *satisfied* in the quote above with the word *content*. Reread it.

5. Write Ecclesiastes 5:10 (NASB) below, substituting the word *content* for the word *satisfied*.

The NLT Parallel Study Bible says of this verse, "Because we were created as spiritual and not just physical beings, possessions and wealth can never satisfy us."[27]

- A closet, or numerous closets, full of clothes will not bring true **contentment**.

- We were meant for something deeper than stuff and things—shoes, dresses, and jeans!

- "Make sure that your character is free from the love of money, being **content** with what you have; for He Himself has said, "I will never desert you, nor will I ever forsake you" (Hebrews 13:5 NASB).

[26]Charles Spurgeon, https://www.goodreads.com/quotes/189188-you-say-if-i-had-a-little-more-i-should
[27]NLT Parallel Study Bible (Carol Stream, Illinois: Tyndale House Publishing, 2011). P. 1145

- You see, whether we have little or much, we are to be **content**. We are to be grateful in both, and that is a daily choice.

The remarkable thing is, we have a choice everyday regarding the attitude we will embrace for that day.[28]
—Chuck Swindoll

Arthur and Wilda had to choose daily to trust God, to wait for Him to deliver, and to be **content**. It is written about them, "Trial upon trial; as the ground (their human comforts) grew so parched with drought that it threatened to crack open, their leaf was still green. Every evening the sound of singing and praise to their Lord ascended. All the courtyard had heard Arthur receive the news that the milk for his little girl would be discontinued due to lack of funds; yet that very evening, they not only sang. But the song of praise had an exultant ring to it!"[29]

In their little they praised! Can you praise God in your little? It is easy to praise Him in our much, our abundance, but what about in times of little?

J. Oswald Sanders says of the Mathew's story, "This poignant story was written to the glory of God and to demonstrate what He can be to those who gladly embrace His will and accept His discipline, no matter how inscrutable (impossible to understand)."[30]

Oh that our story, the one God is writing with each one of our lives, would reflect a heart of gratitude, **contentment**, and glory to Him—whether in little or much!

PONDER:

All our discontents about what we want appear to me to
spring from the lack of thankfulness for what we have.
—Author Unknown

MEDITATE:

Better is the little of the righteous than the abundance of many wicked.
Psalm 37:16 NASB

PRAY:

Oh, Lord, I am so ashamed of my appetite for more. Help me to be satisfied (content)
with Your provisions, whether little or much. I desire to choose daily contentment
over discontentment. You know my heart and what is best for me. May I always have
a heart of praise and thankfulness, giving You glory for Your continual provisions.
Amen!

[28]Chuck Swindoll, brainyquotes.com/Chuck Swindoll
[29]Isobel Kuhn, *Green Leaf in Drought* (Littleton, Colorado: Overseas Missionary Fellowship, Inc., 2010). P. 110
[30]Isobel Kuhn, *Green Leaf in Drought* (Littleton, Colorado: Overseas Missionary Fellowship, Inc., 2010). P. 6

Day Five

I recently bought a book called *Brain Food* by Lisa Mosconi, PhD. As I began to read the first few chapters, I was drowning in scientific facts. A neurosurgeon would have easily understood every word, but not a former kindergarten teacher. All I wanted was for her to tell me **how** to improve my brain function with my diet. I wanted a plan—steps to accomplish my goal.

Knowing the **how** of a job, goal, or project helps us be successful in accomplishing it. This week, we have acknowledged that we all struggle with being **content**, whether in the way we look, with the things we have, or in little or much. Realizing our struggle, we want a plan; we want to know the how of being **content** in each and every state, right? Paul found it in jail and now we want to find it!

1. Fill in the following blanks: "I don't say this out of _____, for I have learned to be _____ in whatever circumstances I am. I know both how to have a _____, and I know how to have _____ In _____ and all _____ I have learned the _____ of being _____ whether well fed or hungry, whether in abundance or in need" (Philippians 4:11-12 HCSB).

Paul "learned" to be **content**. The definition of learning is *knowledge acquired through experience, study, or being taught.* We learn by studying, through instruction, or by what we have experienced. Paul studied the ministry of Jesus, taught His Word, and gained knowledge through his experiences.

Do you remember learning your multiplication facts in the third grade? In order to learn them, my girls and my grandchildren each made index cards with the different facts written on each one. Day in and day out they reviewed their cards. It took discipline, effort, and hard work, but they eventually learned their facts. Learning requires effort on our part. Paul made the effort and God rewarded him for his effort—he gained **contentment**, not a little but enough for each and every situation he faced!

Ask yourself, am I willing to make the effort to learn the secret, the **how**, of being **content**?

I wish I could give you the **how** for finding your **contentment**. But, because I believe the secret for discovering true **contentment** is a work of the heart and a submitting to the Holy Spirit's control of our *wants* and *desires*—I can't—but He can!

What I can give you are some practical and spiritual "helps" for finding your way to **contentment**.

But first, let's look at what does or does not bring us **contentment**, remembering that **contentment** is *showing satisfaction with one's possessions, status, or situation.*

What is it that brings us true **contentment**?

- Is it our looks? No, because they are prone to **change**.

- Is it our stuff? No, because those are prone to **change**.

- Is it our circumstances? No, because they are prone to **change**.

- Is it our financial status? No, because it is prone to **change**.

- Is it our relationships? No, because they are prone to **change**.

- Is it our job? No, because that is prone to **change**.

2. Write the definition of the word **change**.

The word **discontent** is obviously the opposite of **contentment**, it means *a lack of satisfaction with one's possessions, status, or situation; lack of **contentment***.

- If your job changes (goes in a different course or direction), you might find yourself lacking satisfaction with your status—according to the definition of discontent above.

- If your stuff changes (to make different in some particular way), due to wear and tear, you might find yourself lacking satisfaction with your stuff—according to the definition of discontent above.

- If your relationship with a friend changes (goes in a different course or direction), you might find yourself lacking satisfaction with your situation—according to the definition of discontent above.

Life is always changing and in the midst of the change we must **learn** to be **content**, as Paul did.

Paul learned how to be satisfied (**content**) whether he had plenty or was in need. His secret was drawing on Christ's power for strength.

---

*Real **contentment** must come from within. You and I cannot change or control
the world around us, but we can change and control the world within us.*[31]
—Warren W. Wiersbe

---

3. In reading this quote ask God to show you how it applies to your life. Write what He revealed to you below.

[31]Warren W. Wiersbe, The Bumps Are What You Climb On: Encouragement for
Difficult Days (Ada, Michigan: Revell Publishing, 2006). P.152

So, now let's look at some practical and spiritual "helps" for finding your way to **contentment**.

PRACTICAL:

- Stay off Amazon! It is filled with things and stuff we may want or desire—but cannot afford.

- Stay away from wasting time meandering around a mall, Pinterest, Facebook, or hanging out at Target. When you have extra time, invest it in doing something for someone in need.

- Stay in the Word. Replace thoughts of greed and jealousy with scripture.

- Learn to rejoice with friends who get a new home, a new car, larger television, or who own a condo in a tropical place.

- Make a list of everything you have to be thankful for, you will be amazed!

- Start a Blessing box. Periodically write down a blessing you have experienced or been given and place it in the box. When feeling **discontent**, read through your blessing cards.

SPIRITUAL:

- Take every thought captive! Memorize verses such as 2 Corinthians 10:4-5 or Philippians 4:11-12. Bring them to mind when a thought of **discontentment**, envy, jealousy, or greed enter your mind.

- Deepen your spiritual roots through study of the Word, fellowship with other believers, and through prayer.

- Choose **contentment**. It is a daily choice. Life changes, it has its ups and downs. If your **contentment** is dependent upon your life's circumstances, you will be like an emotional roller coaster.

- Daily remind yourself of how blessed you are in comparison to millions around the world who have no roof over their heads, clean water, or food to eat.

- Choose a spirit of gratitude and praise, it will make all the difference!

The secret for discovering true **contentment** comes in allowing God to do a new work in our hearts as we submit our *wants* and *desires* to the Holy Spirit's control.

Arthur Mathews served in China for eleven years and four of those years were spent under house arrest. He was one of the last missionaries to leave the work there in 1953. His life and writings reflected a heart of self-denial and a willingness to embrace God's plans and purposes. He learned to be **content** even in the most difficult of circumstances. As did Paul, writing the words in Philippians from jail.

PONDER:

*We would worry less if we praised more. Thanksgiving is the enemy of **discontent** and dissatisfaction.*[32]
—H. A. Ironside

MEDITATE:

Better a little with righteousness than great income with injustice.
Proverbs 16:8

PRAY:

Father, only You are the true source of contentment for my life.
Circumstances change, but You never do! The work of the heart
needed for me to find contentment in each and every situation can
only be accomplished by You. I submit to Your Spirit's work in me.
May I have a heart of self-denial, embracing all You desire for me.
Amen!

[32]H. A. Ironside, https://www.goodreads.com/quotes/189180-we-would-worry-less-if-we-praised-more

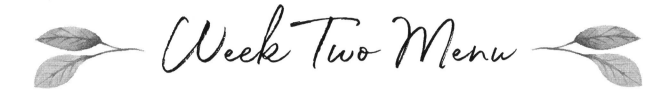

Week Two Menu

Baked Ziti with Italian Sausage

1 tablespoon salt

1 pound ziti

2 tablespoons olive oil

1 small onion, finely chopped

3 tablespoons garlic, minced

2 pounds ground sweet Italian sausage

1 (28 ounce) can tomatoes, petite diced

2 (6 ounce) jars pesto

1 (32 ounce) Ricotta cheese

2 tablespoons butter, softened

2 cups Mozzarella cheese, shredded, divided

1½ cups Parmesan cheese, grated, divided

Preheat oven to 375°F. Over high heat, bring a pot of salt and water to a boil. Add Ziti and cook until al dente. Drain and set aside. Over medium heat, in a large deep skillet, sauté onion and garlic. Once tender, add sausage and cook until browned. Stir in canned tomatoes and pesto, reduce heat to low and simmer for 10 minutes. In large bowl, mix Ricotta, 1½ cups Mozzarella, and 1 cup Parmesan cheese until combined. Butter 9x13 inch baking dish, add al dente pasta. Pour sausage mixture over pasta, spread cheese mixture on top of sausage. Sprinkle top with remaining shredded Mozzarella and Parmesan cheese. Bake for 30 to 40 minutes until heated through and golden brown. <u>Note</u>: Penne pasta can be substituted for ziti.

Simple Italian Salad

DRESSING:

1 teaspoon garlic powder

1 teaspoon dried basil

½ cup olive oil

1 teaspoon dried oregano

½ teaspoon salt

2 tablespoons red wine vinegar

Make ahead and chill. Place all the ingredients in a jar with a tight-fitting lid. Shake vigorously until all ingredients are combined. Store in refrigerator for up to a week. Shake before use.

SALAD:

1 head Romaine lettuce, torn in bite-size pieces

¾ cup Parmesan cheese, grated

½ cup black olives, sliced

Pepper to taste

½ small red onion, thinly sliced

1 cup Pepperoncini, sliced

1 pint cherry tomatoes, sliced

Croutons

Place all ingredients in a large salad bowl. Drizzle with dressing and toss to combine. <u>Note</u>: Pepperoncini found in deli of grocery store.

Lemon Fluff

1½ cups sugar, divided

¼ teaspoon cream of tartar

4 eggs, room temperature, separated

3 tablespoons fresh lemon juice

1 tablespoon lemon rind, grated

2 cups of heavy cream, whipped and divided

1 pint strawberries or raspberries

Preheat oven to 350°F. Sift together 1 cup of sugar and cream of tartar. In mixing bowl, beat egg whites until stiff, gradually adding sugar mixture. Continue beating until thoroughly blended. Line a 9-inch pie plate with parchment paper or dust with baking powder. Line the bottom and the sides of the pie plate with the meringue mixture. Do not spread too close to the edges. Bake until lightly brown. Cool completely. Slightly beat egg yolks, stir in ½ cup sugar, lemon juice, and lemon rind. Cook in a double boiler, stirring constantly, until very thick (8 to 10 minutes). Cool completely. Combine ½ of the whipped cream with lemon mixture. Fill meringue shell. Place the fruit on top of lemon filling and top with the remaining whipped cream. Chill for 24 hours. Note: The pie may also be frozen; however wait to top with the whipped cream until removing from freezer.

Coconut Lemon Bars

CRUST:

1 cup all-purpose flour

¼ cup sugar

½ teaspoon salt

¾ cup butter, chilled and sliced

½ cup coconut, toasted

FILLING:

¾ cup sugar

2 eggs, room temperature

3 tablespoons lemon juice

1 tablespoon lemon zest

½ teaspoon baking powder

½ teaspoon salt

Confectioners' Sugar, dust top

Preheat oven to 350°F. In food processor, combine flour, sugar, and salt until mixed. Add butter and coconut, processing until mixture resembles a fine meal. Line an 8-inch square pan with parchment paper. Lightly butter the parchment paper. Transfer the flour crumb mixture to pan and press into bottom forming a crust. Bake until light golden brown around the edges, about 20 minutes. For filling, combine sugar, eggs, lemon juice, zest, baking powder, and salt in food processor or blender. Process until smooth. Pour filling into hot crust. Continue to bake until the filling begins to brown around the edges and springs back when touched, about 25 to 30 minutes. Cool on rack. Lift parchment paper from pan and cut into squares.

SHORT-CUTS ...

- **BAKED ZITI WITH ITALIAN SAUSAGE:** Casserole may be prepared, sealed tightly and refrigerated three to four days ahead of baking time.

- **SHREDDING CHEESE:** Day before or earlier in the day, shred all cheeses necessary for entrée and salad. You will be glad you did! But, easier than this, buy the cheese shredded.

- **SIMPLE ITALIAN SALAD AND DRESSING:** Prepare the salad dressing a day or two before serving and refrigerate. Wash and prepare lettuce and all veggies the morning prior to serving. Place in zipper-lock bags and refrigerate. The salad can be assembled 2 to 4 hours ahead. Top with Parmesan cheese just prior to serving.

- **CRISP GREENS:** Look for greens that are crisp and free of blemishes. When arriving home from grocery store, wash and dry, then store by wrapping in dry paper towels in a tightly sealed plastic bag. One pound of greens yields 6 cups of torn lettuce.

- **LEMON FLUFF** can be made several days ahead of time and frozen. Wait to top with the whipped cream until just before serving. Coconut Lemon Bars can be made a day ahead.

HEALTHY TIPS ...

- **BAKED ZITI WITH ITALIAN SAUSAGE:** If you can find nitrate-free Italian sausage, use it.

- **GLUTEN-FREE:** If gluten intolerant, purchase gluten-free ziti or leave out the pasta and bake meat mixture in casserole dish. <u>Note</u>: Gluten-free Penne pasta may be substituted for Ziti.

- **REDUCED FAT OPTION:** Reduce the amount of cheese called for in casserole to half. Recipe will not be as cheesy, but you will have less fat and cholesterol.

- **BLOCKS OF CHEESE:** Purchase blocks of cheese and shred instead of using pre-shredded cheese. Harmful chemicals are used in order to preserve pre-shredded cheese and give it a longer shelf life. Shredding your own will be healthier.

- **SIMPLE ITALIAN SALAD:** The darker the greens the healthier. For example, Romaine, Spinach (green and red leaf), Watercress, and Arugula are great options.

- **LEMON FLUFF AND COCONUT LEMON BARS:** These two lemon recipes may not be considered the most healthy desserts because they contain sugar. However, it is not as large an amount compared to some desserts—like the one in Week One! So just eat and enjoy!

Voices

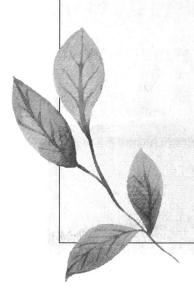

The willingness to obey every word from God
is critical to hearing God speak.
—Henry T. Blackaby

Voices Introduction

*Y*ears ago, Mark and I would often drive to the lake in Oklahoma where his parents owned a small cabin. One of our favorite things to do was to take the boat out in the evening and find a cove in which to anchor. There is no *quiet* like the *quiet* found on a lake in the evening as the sun is setting. We would lay on the front of the boat watching the stars as they began to appear in the sky. It was still, peaceful, and serene. In the *quiet* of that cove we were attuned to the sounds of the crickets on the shore, and the fish as they skimmed the surface of the lake. Because of the stillness of that place we were aware of our surroundings and attentive to the incredible sounds of creation. It was as if God was speaking through His creation.

When we **choose** to be **still**, He speaks through the quiet of a morning sunrise, a hike in the woods, an evening boat ride on the lake, a walk in a spring rain, and in the stillness of a quiet time chair each morning. Sometimes He whispers, sometimes He thunders, and sometimes He speaks purposefully and forcefully in order to get our full attention.

In the Psalm 29, David describes the **voice** of God in this manner, "The **voice** of the Lord echoes from the clouds. The God of glory thunders through the skies. So powerful is His voice; so full of majesty. It breaks down the cedars. It splits the giant trees of Lebanon. It shakes Mount Lebanon and Mount Sirion. They leap and skip before him like young calves! The voice of the Lord thunders through the lightning. It resounds through the deserts and shakes the wilderness of Kadesh. The voice of the Lord spins and topples the mighty oaks. It strips the forests bare. They whirl and sway beneath the blast. But in his Temple all are praising, 'Glory, glory to the Lord.' At the flood the Lord showed his control of all creation. Now he continues to unveil his power. He will give his people strength. He will bless them with peace" (Psalm 29:3-11 The Living Bible).

After Mark's death, I found it very hard to adjust to the quiet of our home. I am not sure I will ever adjust to the *deafening* silence of a house with one occupant. Yet, because God always works good into the hardest of situations, due to the quiet, I am able to hear His **voice** more clearly and feel His presence more intensely. What I have discovered is that He is always present and desires companionship and communication with us. But, our homes, hearts, and lives are filled with activity, **distractions**, and noise—noise and **distractions** that drown out His **voice** and busyness that replaces His companionship.

At times, I am tempted to be pulled away from the Creator's **voice** due to life's busyness and **distractions**. Other times, I am tempted to listen to the voices of others. And then there is the enemy who beckons me to listen to his **voice** or the **voice** of the world. There are so many **voices** that compete for our time and attention. The **voice** to which we choose to listen will determine the direction of our lives. If we will choose to tune out the **voices** of others and listen to our Creator, He will give us wisdom, direction, strength, and peace.

> *Listen in silence because if your heart is full of other things you cannot hear the voice of God.*[33]
> *—Mother Teresa*

[33]Mother Teresa, bing.com/images/Mother Teresa

Day One

In Mother Teresa's quote found in the Introduction, she said, "listen in silence." How do we accomplish this in a world that is filled with a variety of **voices** vying for a place in our minds, hearts, and lives? When is the last time you truly experienced pure unadulterated silence? Now that I am a widow, I have no problem experiencing silence. Often, I purposely turn on the television just to hear the **voices** of others. But, what about the young college student living in a dorm or an apartment with roommates, or the young married woman with a job, a new home, and husband to care for, or the young mom with small children who are incessantly whining or asking her questions? Where do they find silence, an escape from the busy schedule and the continual sound of **voices** speaking into their lives?

In order to listen we must **be silent**, attentive, and **positioned** correctly, we must **be still**.

1. Are **being still** and **being silent** the same thing? Yes_____ No_____. Explain.

2. Fill in the blanks of the following verse: "Be _____, and _____ that I am _____! I will be honored by every nation. I will be honored throughout the world" (Psalm 46:10a NLT).

The definition of the word **still** is *devoid of or abstaining from motion*. In other words, we are to be motionless in order to truly **be still** and **positioned** to listen!

3. Fill in the blanks of the following verse: "Teach me, and I will be_____; make me _____ how I have gone astray" (Job 6:24 ESV).

The definition of the word **silent** is *making no utterance, not speaking or making noise*. In other words, we are not to speak a word—just listen!

Mother Teresa went on to say, "**If** your heart is full of **other things** you cannot hear the voice of God." Let's substitute a few different phrases for the word **if**:

*   **In the event** that your heart is full of **other things** you cannot hear the **voice** of God.

*   **Allowing that** your heart is full of **other things** you cannot hear the **voice** of God.

*   **On the assumption** that your heart is full of **other things** you cannot hear the **voice** of God.

*   **On condition** that your heart is full of **other things** you cannot hear the **voice** of God.

4. Does using the different phrases help you understand the "**if**" used by Mother Teresa? Yes_____ No_____. Explain.

5. Do you think she was making the assumption that we all have **other things** that fill our hearts and keep us from hearing God's voice? Yes_____ No_____

6. What are some of the **other things** that fill your heart and distract you from hearing God's voice?

In the rush and noise of life, as you have intervals, step home within yourselves and be still.
Wait upon God, and feel His good presence; this will carry you evenly through your day's business.[34]
—William Penn

---

7. Jesus experienced "intervals" in His life and ministry that carried Him through His daily "business" of ministry. Read the following verses. Note the places where Jesus found silence and solitude in order to hear the Father's **voice**.

VERSE IN THE NIV:	PLACE OF SILENCE AND SOLITUDE:
Mark 1:35	
Luke 5:15-16	
Luke 6:12	
Mark 6:31-32	
Matthew 14:13	
Matthew 26:36	

Solitude means *being alone or remote from others—secluded.* Because we have chosen to live **hurried** lives, finding solitude is often impossible. Can you imagine what would happen if we chose to live daily **unhurried** lives in solitude with the Father? We would actually experience peace and quiet, be able to hear His **voice** more clearly, have an inward joy, receive wisdom for living, and bask in the grace He offers. At times, Jesus chose to set Himself aside from His **hurried** life of ministry. Even though His days here on earth were short, He took the time to step away in order to hear from the Father, will you?

PONDER:

The more quiet we are the more attentive we are to the Lord's voice.
—Author Unknown

MEDITATE:

For thus said the Lord God, the Holy One of Israel, 'In returning and rest you shall be saved; in quietness and in trust shall be your strength.' But you were unwilling ...
Isaiah 30:15 ESV

PRAY:

Father, I want to "listen in silence" upon emptying my heart of the "other things" that hinder me from hearing Your voice. Help me to follow Jesus' example in choosing silence and solitude. Remove the commitments from my hurried life that stand between me and what You have for me. I want to position myself to hear You.
Amen!

Day Two

We were coming back to Memphis from Oklahoma on Interstate 40, and as we neared the sixty mile marker, the traffic came to a halt. As I slowed, I noticed several semitrailers swiftly exiting the highway. I made a split-second decision to follow, assuming they knew where they were going, and that their destination was the same as ours. I trusted the truckers to get us where we needed to go. They obviously knew the Optional road and had traveled it before. The two-lane highway ran parallel to Interstate 40. Once we had driven about forty miles, we re-entered the interstate long past the construction and were home free.

Fortunately for us, following the semitrailer drivers worked out well. We didn't get lost and even arrived at our desired destination. But, often in following or listening to the **voices of others**, we can become lost in life. There are several examples in the Bible of those who **listened** to the **voices of others** and to their own detriment. Job is one of those. His friends were pretty determined that they knew what God was up to in his life, and how he should handle his circumstances. Job himself wrestled with the circumstances God was allowing in his life. If you read the entire book, you will see that Job, like his friends, spoke of God in ignorance. But he acknowledged his wrong doing, when he said of God, "I know that you can do anything, and no one can stop you" (Job 42:1-6 NLT).

Sometimes the **voices** that clamor for our undivided attention can speak in ignorance, as Job and his friends did. We must remember that man is flawed and often so is his **advice**! On occasion when we follow the **voices of others**, we can end up in challenging circumstances.

Today, we will look at an example in God's Word of a family member's **voice** that was wise and worth heeding and a friend's **voice** that should have been considered unwise and disregarded.

Read Exodus 18:13-23 (HCSB Recommended).

1. Was the advice Jethro gave Moses wise or unwise? Explain.

2. What was the result of Jethro's advice to Moses?

> *Jethro's visit not only reunited Moses with his family and directed the Israelite leaders to worship together; he also provided a solution to an overwhelming problem.[35] The Study Bible for Women HCSB*

[35]*The Study Bible for Women* HCSB (Nashville, Tennessee: Holman Bible Publishers, 2014). P. 90

3. Fill in the blanks of the following verse: "But the _____ from above is first pure, then peaceable, gentle, open to reason, _____ of mercy and good fruits, impartial and _____" (James 3:17 ESV).

Read 2 Samuel 13:1-20.

4. Was the advice Jonadab gave Amnon wise or unwise? Explain.

5. What was the result of Jonadab's advice to Amnon?

It is obvious that Jethro sought the wisdom of God and Amnon did not. When we listen to the **voices of others** and when we give **advice**, we should be most certain that the **advice** is rooted in God's Word and is God-given wisdom.

Maybe for you the **voices of others** includes your family, friends, in-laws, pastors, or church leaders. Jesus **tuned out** the **voices of others** and found solitude and silence in order to **tune in** to His Father's **voice** of wisdom. He knew that removing himself from the **voices of others**, would allow him to focus on what the Father had for him. How could we think that we can live well without following Jesus' example?

Like Jesus, we must empty our lives of the **other things** in order to be **positioned** to listen. Over the years of Mark's illness, one of the **other things** we had to empty ourselves of were the **voices** of those around us. God had chosen a different path for us and many wanted to weigh in as to what we were to do. It was not easy to choose solitude in order to **position** ourselves to hear His **voice**, but we were grateful we did. Because we chose to be still and set ourselves apart, we could hear Him clearly and obey His directives for our lives.

6. Fill in the blank of the following verse: "Be _____ before the Lord, all mankind, because he has roused himself from his holy dwelling" (Zechariah 2:13 NIV).

 [36]*NLT Parallel Study Bible* (Carol Stream, Illinois: Tyndale House Publishing, 2011). P.138

We must be willing to follow Jesus' example. He chose solitude, silence, stillness, and properly **positioning** himself in order to hear the Father's voice and then obeyed what God was asking of Him as His Son.

7. What changes do you need to make in order to have solitude and silence, **positioning** yourself to hear the Father's voice?

Jesus continually withdrew from people, daily life activities, and the demands of his ministry to be alone with the Father and pray. He had an ongoing, intimate relationship with His Father that was the source of His compassion, mercy, grace, wisdom, and power. Because He chose separation from the world (**voices of others**) around Him, Jesus enjoyed a regular time of talking to God and listening to His Word (**voice**).

PONDER:

If we are to be just like Jesus, we must have regular time talking to God and listening to his Word.[37]
—Max Lucado

MEDITATE:

But the Lord is in his holy Temple. Let all the earth be silent before him.
Habakkuk 2:20 NLT

PRAY:

Father, help me to be wise and discerning when listening to the voices of others.
Although, those I love feel they have my best interest in mind, they do not know what
Your best is for my life. Speak to me through Your Word and the Holy Spirit,
leading me in the way You would have me to go.
Amen!

[37]Max Lucado, https://www.quoteschristian.com/justlikejesus.html

Day Three

The week of March 8th, 2020, was an historical week as we watched the NBA, along with numerous other sports organizations, shut down due to the possible spread of a new virus called COVID-19. That week, we began to hear a variety of **voices** speaking into our lives, like Dr. Fauci, our President and Vice-President, Governors, Mayors, and local officials, along with government organizations, such as the CDC and your local health department. Friends, Facebook, Twitter, and news networks brought even more **voices** speaking into our lives. We were told there would be numbers of deaths into the millions or above and devastation like nothing we had seen since the Spanish flu of 1918.

During the first week, I found myself concerned as a result of what I was hearing and even fearful. I found it hard to discern all the **voices** speaking into my life. Never before had I had so many **voices** vying for my attention and my loyalty. Because of that, I **positioned** myself to listen to all the **voices** of the world rather than to God's **voice**.

The **voices** of the world can be demanding, forceful, misleading, demeaning, deceitful, and discouraging. Why? Because often the **author** of those **voices** is Satan himself. And even when he is not the author, he will find a way to take what someone has said to mislead, demean, defeat, and discourage you. He is crafty. He will turn around the words spoken to you through the **voices** of the world in order to entice you, deceive you, change your heart, and your biblical perspective on life.

1. Fill in the blanks of the following verse:"You are of your father the _____, and your will is to do your father's desires. He was a _____ from the beginning, and has _____ to do with the _____, because there is no _____ in him. When he _____, he speaks out of his own character, for he is a _____ and the father of _____" (John 8:44 ESV).

Max Lucado said, "Two types of voices command your attention today. Negative ones fill your mind with doubt, bitterness, and fear. Positive ones purvey hope and strength. Which one will you choose to heed?"[38]

The Bible says that Satan is the commander of the powers of the unseen world and the father of lies (Revelation 20:1-2). Therefore, his **voice** is typically negative and brings about negative results. On the other hand, God's Word resonates with hope, strength, wisdom, peace, and clarity.

2. Read Proverbs 16:20 and Luke 11:28 in the ESV. What word describes the gift given those who read, hear, and trust the Word (voice) of God? Fill in the letters below to form the correct word. ___l__s___e___!

God is ready to speak if I am ready to listen.
So, I'll turn down the volume of the noise that is within me to hear Him.
—Author Unknown

[38]Max Lucado, *"Live Loved: Experiencing God's Presence in Everyday Life."* (Nashville, Tennessee: Thomas Nelson Books, Inc., 2011). P. 222

In the beginning of the virus outbreak, I had **positioned** myself to listen to all the **voices** of the world rather than to God's **voice**. Finally, I realized that I needed to "turn down the volume of the noise within me" as a result of listening to other **voices**, and hear from my Father.

3. What are some circumstances or reasons that cause us to **position** ourselves to hear the world's many **voices** more intently than God's voice?

Often while traveling between Memphis, where I live, and my daughter's home in Texas, I listen to Christian radio. As long as I am within the range of a tower the reception is good, but as I get further and further away, the reception is just static and fuzz. The **voices** of those speaking or singing become unclear. In spiritual terms, the further away we get from God's **voice** the more unclear life becomes.

4. Tell of a time when you listened to the **voices** of the world rather than God's voice. What were the results? What lesson did you learn?

> *Then they knelt before him in mockery and taunted, 'Hail! King of the Jews.'*
> *The people passing by shouted abuse, shaking their heads in mockery.*
> *The leading priests, the teachers of religious law, and the elders also mocked Jesus.*
> *Matthew 27:29b, 39, 41 NLT*

On the pathway to suffering, and as Jesus hung dying on the cross, He had a great many **voices** shouting at Him. He was resolute in fulfilling His purpose and in His relationship with the Father. He was attentive to the Father's **voice**, purpose, and presence as He hung there **positioned** between two thieves sweating drops of blood. The only One he wanted to please was His Father.

We must be willing to follow Jesus' example in tuning out the **voices** of the world and in seeking solitude, silence, stillness, and properly **positioning** ourselves in order to hear the Father's **voice**. In doing so, we like Jesus, will fulfill the Father's purpose for our lives. Jesus' purpose was to provide a way of salvation for all of mankind. If you **position** yourself and listen attentively, He will speak and reveal your purpose!

PONDER:

*Only as we learn to hear the voice of the Father can we learn to dispel the **voices** of the world.*[39]
—Dick Eastman

MEDITATE:

Blessed are those who listen to me, watching daily at my doors, waiting at my doorway.
Proverbs 8:34 NIV

PRAY:

Heavenly Father, Your voice is as gentle and quiet as the shepherd's voice
that gently and lovingly calls his sheep by name. Guard my heart and mind against
the need to listen to the voices of the world. May Your voice be heard above all the
the voices around me. I desire to position myself to hear and obey Your will and purpose
for my life. May I be the sheep who follows her shepherd because she knows His voice!
Amen!

 [39]Dick Eastman, *The Hour that Changes the World* (Grand Rapids, Michigan: Baker Book House Company, 2002). P 113

Day Four

I can't tell you how many times over the years, while shopping with my girls, I heard a child across the store call out, "mommy," and I answered thinking it was one of them. Just to discover that the **voice** calling out was not looking for me. If I had taken the time to **discern** the **voice**, I would have known it was not one of mine.

1. Write the dictionary definition of word **discernment** below.

The Biblical definition of the word discernment is the *ability to decide between truth and error, right and wrong.* **Discernment** is *the process of making careful distinctions in our thinking about truth.* In other words, the ability to think with discernment is synonymous with an ability to think biblically.[40]

> *The Spirit clearly says that in later times some will abandon the faith*
> *and follow **deceiving** spirits and things taught by demons.*
> *1 Timothy 4:1 NIV*

You need to be **discerning** in order not to follow the **voices** of **deceiving spirits**. Another word for **discernment** is **wisdom**.

2. What does James 1:5 tell us about the source of **wisdom**?

Read Ephesians 1:15-18.

3. In his letter to the church of Ephesus, what did Paul say would be the benefit of spiritual wisdom and insight?

[40]https://www.christianity.com/theology/what-is-biblical-discernment-and-why-is-it-important-11532182.html

Paul said, "I pray for you constantly, asking God, the glorious Father of our Lord Jesus Christ, to give you spiritual wisdom and insight that you might grow in your knowledge of God."

Without wisdom, **discernment**, and knowledge of God's Word, we will be led astray by **deceiving spirits**. Those **deceiving spirits** come in all different forms. When making decisions related to things you have heard or are told, you must compare what you heard or are told with the Word of God, and you must ask is it truth or error, right or wrong? Let the Word help you discern truth from lies and falsehood.

In the Old Testament, the people relied upon the Priests and Prophets who taught the Word of God for gaining knowledge and **discernment** into all truth. In the New Testament, Jesus and his disciples were the teachers of the Word of God. They taught the people how to **discern** between God's **voice** (Word) and the **voices** of the **deceiving** sprits. Once Jesus had completed His time on this earth, God sent the Holy Spirit to live in the heart and life of every believer. The Holy Spirit helps all believers discern between the voices of others, the **voices** of the world, the **voice** of Satan, and the **voice** of God.

Read Genesis 48:1-21 for an Old Testament example of a man who grew in his ability to discern as he grew in his relationship with God.

"Many times **discernment** is gained only by difficult experiences. This seems to be the case with many saints, especially Jacob. In his earlier years he went through many difficulties because he was so strong and trusted in his own abilities. However, in his later years when his natural sight was almost gone, he exercised amazing **discernment**. By this time he no longer trusted his natural sense, or the preference of others, but he **perceived God's mind** for the future of his sons. He clearly sensed God's mind concerning his grandsons and crossed his arms to lay his right hand on the younger child."[41]

As with Jacob (Israel), our natural strength must be broken. Our trust must shift from our own ability and personal insight to total dependence on the Lord. Once this occurs, we will begin to **discern** that still small **voice** that makes known His mind and His will.

4. Fill in the blanks of John 16:13-15: "But when the _____ of truth comes, he will _____ you into all the truth. He will not speak on his own. He will speak only what he _____. And he will tell you what is still going to happen. He will bring me _____. That's because what he receives from me he will _____ to you. Everything that belongs to the Father is mine. That is why I said what the _____ receives from me he will _____ to you (NIRV)."

As Jesus neared His trial and crucifixion, He promised his apostles that He would ask God to send them His Holy Spirit. The Holy Spirit would remain with them after Jesus died, was resurrected, and returned to the Father.

In John 14:15-18, we see that Jesus promised the Holy Spirit would teach the disciples and remind them of everything that Jesus had already taught them. The Holy Spirit is the present-day advocate of Jesus Christ living in the heart of every believer. He instructs us, **discerns** truth for us, guides us, teaches us, and strengthens us.

[41]http://www.bibloscope.com/content/kaleidosopic-views/biblical-examples-dsicernment

It is the spirit of God, in the person of the Holy Spirit. The **voice** of the Holy Spirit is the most important **voice** you need to hear because it speaks the mind of God. The **voice** of the Holy Spirit will guard your heart and mind against Satan and his **deceiving spirits**. The voice of the Holy Spirit, unlike all the other voices that speak into your heart and life, is a wise and **discerning** voice. You would do well to heed it!

As we close today, I want to quickly chart the difference between **condemnation**, which is always the **voice** of Satan, and **conviction**, which is the **gentle voice** of God calling you to repentance. God never belittles us, condemns us, or accuses us—those tactics are of Satan. God, through the convicting power of the Holy Spirit, gently breaks our heart over our sin, and calls us back into fellowship with Him. You need to be aware of the difference between the two.

CONVICTION BY THE HOLY SPIRIT:

1. **Definite and specific**. The Lord tells me exactly what to say.

2. **Recognizable**. It is something unconfessed and unforgiven that I recognize—usually in the immediate past.

3. **Definite solution**. The Holy Spirit tells me how to take care of sin. When I obey, I get relief from soul-pain guilt.

CONDEMNATION BY SATAN:

1. **Indefinite and vague**. I feel guilty, but cannot identify sin.

2. **Imaginary**. I have a hard time putting my finger on this—unless it is something in the past that I have already taken care of.

3. **Usually no solution**. If any solution is offered, it is irrational and unscriptural. The soul pain intensifies.[42] —Peter Lord

PONDER:

Train your mind to hear what God whispers and not what the enemy may be shouting.
—Author Unknown

MEDITATE:

The sum of your words is truth, and every one of your righteous rules endures forever.
Psalm 119:160 ESV

PRAY:

Father, You are the God of all truth. Satan is a liar and deceiver.
I am grateful that Your truth continually sanctifies and protects my
mind from the lies of Satan and his deceiving spirits. Daily protect my
mind and heart from deceptive thoughts and emotions. May I know Your
truth and speak Your truth in the face of lies, thus causing the enemy to flee!
Amen!

[42]Peter Lord, *Hearing God* (Grand Rapids, Michigan: Baker Book House Company, 1988). P. 130

Day Five

For years, when we would visit my in-laws, my mother-in-law would busy herself in the kitchen with preparations for each meal. She would invariably ask my girls questions about their school, church, activities, sports, friends, etc. Since we lived miles apart, it was very kind of her to take an interest. The problem came when my girls went to answer her questions. She was so busy with all the details of the meal she was preparing, the table she was setting, or cleaning up the mess made from preparations that she failed to **listen** to them. Eventually, they would give up, rise from their chair and leave the room; seldom did she even notice.

Please don't take this as a criticism of my mother-in-law as much as an example of how **listening** is more important than activity. She felt she was doing a good thing in preparing a meal for us, and she was. But, my girls wanted her to **listen** to their answers to her questions so she could connect with them emotionally—heart to heart.

1. What does James tell us about listening in James 1:19 NIV?

When we find places of solitude and stillness, and are **positioned** correctly, then we are able to **listen** attentively. My mother-in-law wanted to hear from my girls, the problem was that she was neither **still** nor **positioned** correctly to **listen**. Sitting and being **still** were very difficult for her. Serving was her way of loving on us. Yet, because she would not stop to be **still** and **listen**, she missed opportunities to hear from and connect with her grandchildren.

Being a Martha, I can be guilty of this as well. Watching my mother-in-law over the years, helped me to realize that the activities are not as important as the time spent with others, and time **listening** to their heart. In being still and **listening**, we connect with one another.

When we **position** ourselves to listen, God will speak. He speaks to us primarily through His Word. He also speaks through the Holy Spirit, pastors, and godly teachers. As you listen to pastors and teachers be sure their message aligns accurately with the truth of scripture.

Matthew 11:15 says, "He who has ears to hear, let him hear." This statement made by Jesus is quoted fifteen times in the New Testament. He is saying, "Pay attention! Listen up!" Peter Lord in his book, *Hearing God*, says, This indicates the importance of two things:

#1: "A basic premise: having ears to hear."

#2: "A basic choice: choosing to use those ears to hear."[43]

 [43]Peter Lord, *Hearing God* (Grand Rapids, Michigan: Baker Book House Company, 1988). P. 28

2. Read Acts 16:11-15. Whose life was changed because she chose to sit attentively **hearing** and **listening** to the Word of God being taught? What was the result of her changed heart?

When we **hear**, **listen**, and **obey** the promptings of the Holy Spirit, we are changed—as Lydia was changed.

Remember when I said that if I had taken time to discern the child's **voice** in the store calling for her mommy, I would have known it was not one of my girls? Many of you may be asking, how do I know when it is God's **voice** that is speaking to me? How do I discern His **voice** from Satan's voice or the **voices** of others?

Peter Lord says of this most asked question, "In the thirty-six years of ministry, the question I get asked more than any other is: 'How do you know God's **voice**? How can one know whether the thoughts are God's or from the devil?' This was a question I could never answer fully—because I myself sometimes had the same question. It is a question that, by God's grace, I am now learning to answer for myself and those others who are really wanting to know."[44]

Pastor Lord uses the remaining pages in his book answering this question. Through the years, I struggled with that very question, but like Pastor Lord, I have come to recognize God's **voice** and discern His **voice** versus the **voices** of others and Satan's **voice**.

Let me give you two personal examples:

- In the spring of 2008, I was in line with my grandson at a fast food restaurant. The young man in front of us was a UPS driver. He ordered his lunch but when it was time to pay, he realized he had left his billfold at home. I felt the Lord say, "Pay for his lunch." Normally, this would not have been a big deal. But at the time, Mark was unemployed, had been diagnosed with a rare neurological disease, and we had put our house up for sale because we could no longer afford it. The young man was embarrassed but very grateful for my help. As my grandson and I left, I chuckled to myself thinking how even more embarrassed he would have been if he had known my circumstances.

- How did I know it was God's **voice** and not my own or Satan's **voice**? Let me tell you. I would have felt badly for the young man but because I am fleshly and often self-centered, I would not have thought to buy his lunch. Satan feeds selfishness and not generosity, so it did not come from him. God is a generous God who cares about people. Therefore, He said, "Pay," so I paid. I never missed that money and that is another reason I know it was God.

[44]Peter Lord, Hearing God (Grand Rapids, Michigan: Baker Book House Company, 1988). P. 19

At the beginning of our journey with Mark's illness, he felt the Lord telling him that we were to wait. "Wait for what? I asked him." He was not sure. But, what he was very sure of was that God's word to him was wait. I began the Secrets ministry with his support and blessing. As the ministry grew the first couple of years, people suggested that we apply for a 501c3 designation. Mark was no longer able to work due to the disease but at the time, he was very cognitively sharp. So, he decided to research what was involved in the process. Unfortunately, he discovered that it was quite a lengthy process, with mounds of paperwork, and it was expensive. So, we decided to lay down the idea and move on. Three months later, we got a phone call from an acquaintance of Mark's. He and his wife ran a ministry in town and they ask if we would meet with them. We spent the first few minutes catching up with one another's lives. Then he said, "You are probably wondering why we ask you here. Well, we heard about your ministry and we believe in what you are trying to do, so we want to ask you to pray about coming up under our 501c3 designation." As he said this, I began to cry realizing that this is why God said wait.

> *In our flesh, we are unwillingly to wait. Many times, we find a way to get what we want, when we want it. But, God said wait—He knew waiting would be hard for us. Satan would not ask us to wait because he likes it when we ignore God's **voice** and step out on our own. He knows what a mess we make of our lives when we do not obey. Satan also knows that if we are **willing** to wait, there is nothing God will not do for us.*
> *Isaiah 64:4*

I am grateful for a godly husband that was **still**, and **positioned** himself to **listen** to the Father's **voice**, and obeyed regardless of what others thought. He taught me that I have One **voice** and One alone to listen to, and that is the Father's **voice**.

PONDER:

Spending time with God puts everything else in perspective. —Author Unknown

MEDITATE:

He wakes me up every morning; he makes me alert so I can listen attentively as disciples do.
Isaiah 50:4b NET

PRAY:

Father, I am grateful that as Your child, You long to speak into my life each and every day.
Help me to lay aside the many things that distract and pull me away from Your presence.
Give me a longing heart and a spirit that seeks after You. Help me to be a disciple who listens
attentively as You teach and instruct me in the way I should go. Guard my heart and mind against
all the other voices speaking into my life. I want to hear You and You alone!
Amen!

Week Three Menu

Honey BBQ Tenderloin

2¾ pounds pork tenderloin

¼ cup light, low-sodium soy sauce

5 garlic cloves, minced

½ teaspoon ginger, ground

2 tablespoons brown sugar

3 tablespoons honey

2 teaspoons dark sesame oil

Preheat grill on medium-high at 350°F to 400°F. Make a lengthwise cut down the center of each tenderloin to within ¼ inch of opposite side; press to open. Combine soy sauce, garlic, and ginger in a shallow dish; add tenderloins. Cover and chill 3 to 4 hours, turning occasionally. Stir together brown sugar, honey, and oil. Grill tenderloins, covered with grill lid, for 20 minutes or until a meat thermometer inserted into thickest portion registers 160°, turning occasionally and basting with honey mixture. Heat your favorite BBQ sauce and drizzle over top before serving. Note: Substitute olive oil, coconut oil, or peanut oil for sesame oil.

Golden Potato Casserole

6 large potatoes, your choice

½ cup butter

2 cups Cheddar cheese, shredded

2 cups sour cream

¼ cup green onions, chopped

1½ teaspoons salt

1 teaspoon white pepper

2 tablespoons butter

Preheat oven to 350°F. Peel potatoes. In saucepan over medium high heat, cook the potatoes until tender. Drain. When cooled, shred coarsely. In large saucepan, melt ½ cup butter and Cheddar cheese over low heat. Blend in sour cream, onion, salt, and white pepper. Cook until onion is tender. Add potatoes, toss lightly, and turn into a buttered casserole dish. Dot top with 2 tablespoons butter and bake for 20 to 30 minutes until golden brown.

Green Peas with Buttered Pine Nuts

½ cup chicken broth

2 (10 ounce) packages frozen English peas

3 green onions, cut into ½ inch pieces

½ teaspoon sugar

¾ cup pine nuts

4 tablespoons butter, melted

1 tablespoon fresh rosemary, chopped

Salt and pepper to taste

Bring chicken broth to a boil in a medium saucepan over medium-high heat. Add peas, green onions, and sugar; cover, reduce heat, and simmer 5 minutes or until peas are tender. Drain well, and set aside. Cook pine nuts in butter in a saucepan over medium heat, stirring constantly, 2 to 3 minutes or until golden. Add pea mixture, rosemary, salt, and pepper to taste; cook, uncovered, 2 minutes or until thoroughly heated. Note: Due to the high cost of Pine Nuts, consider using almonds or nut of choice.

Toffee Ice Cream Dessert

3 cups Oreo cookies, crushed

2 tablespoons butter, melted

½ gallon Vanilla ice cream, softened

1 (8 ounce) package Heath toffee bits

Fudge sauce, heated

Optional: Maraschino cherries

Preheat oven to 350°F. Combine chocolate cookie crumbs and butter, stir with fork. Press firmly into bottom of lightly greased 9x13 baking dish. Bake for 5 minutes, cool. Spread half of ice cream over crust; sprinkle with half of toffee chips, repeat layers. Cover and freeze until firm. Cut ice cream into squares to serve. If desired: Top each with a dollop of whipped cream, fudge, and a cherry. Note: Heath toffee bits can be found in the baking section of grocery.

Fudge Sauce

1 cup water

1 cup sugar

1 (4 ounce) bag semisweet chocolate

1 (14 ounce) can sweetened condensed milk

1 pinch salt

1 stick butter

1 teaspoon vanilla

Boil water, sugar, and chocolate in saucepan over medium-high for 5 minutes. Remove from heat and stir in can of sweetened condensed milk and salt. Return to heat and boil 3 to 5 minutes longer. Remove from heat, and stir in butter and vanilla. Cool. Store in refrigerator. May be reheated in microwave on medium power.

SHORT-CUTS...

- **HONEY BBQ TENDERLOIN:** Earlier in the day, or the night before, place tenderloin in marinade and refrigerate until ready to cook, turning occasionally.

- **GOLDEN POTATO CASSEROLE:** Can be made a day or two ahead of serving time. Wrap tightly and refrigerate.

- **GREEN PEAS WITH BUTTERED PINE NUTS:** Earlier in the day, cook pine nuts in butter until golden brown and remove from heat. Set aside until needed.

- **TOFFEE ICE CREAM DESSERT:** Can be made up to 1 to 3 days ahead and stored in freezer. Set out 10 minutes before serving.

- **FUDGE SAUCE:** Fudge sauce can be made up to a week ahead of serving.

HEALTHY TIPS...

- **HONEY BBQ TENDERLOIN:** Use low-sodium or sodium-free soy sauce. Olive, peanut or coconut oil can be substituted for sesame oil. Use raw unfiltered honey. Replace amount of brown sugar called for with equal amount of honey.

- **GOLDEN POTATO CASSEROLE:** Use the finest and purest (cleanest) butter and sour cream. Do not use low-fat ingredients as these have additives. If the manufacturer removes something good from the ingredient to make it lower in fat, they have to replace that good ingredient with a manmade manufactured chemical. Clean and pure is best.

- **GREEN PEAS WITH BUTTERED PINE NUTS:** Use organic chicken broth or homemade.

- **GREEN PEAS WITH BUTTERED PINE NUTS:** Substitute ½ teaspoon sugar for ½ teaspoon raw honey.

- **TOFFEE ICE CREAM DESSERT:** As in any ice cream dessert with an Oreo cookie crust, healthy is not possible—so just indulge and enjoy it!

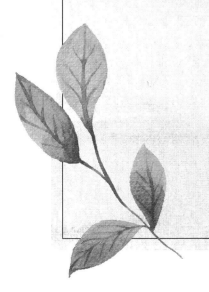

Busyness

This present world system is strategically designed to squeeze out your time and energy for the secret place.

— Bob Sorge

usy, busy, busy, the world is busy! I'm busy—you're busy—everyone is busy! We are all oh so busy! Have you ever considered that **busyness** might be a **distraction** that is keeping you from enjoying the restoration of the soul that is found in solitude and quiet—in the "secret" place?

> *We all need times to unstring the bow of our routine stresses and enjoy the restoration that silence and solitude can provide for our body and soul.*[45]
> —Donald S Whitney

My phone chimed with a new text. I looked down to see that it was a friend asking if she could come by the house to talk. Once she arrived, actually her enthusiasm arrived before she did, I could tell she had good news. Little did I know that it was good for her and for me! She said, "I have a crazy idea. I was wondering if you wanted to go to Destin, Florida this coming Tuesday to hear a friend of mine speak at a church? This was Thursday the week prior. I was waist deep into a writing project. I wondered if I could go and yet keep to the writing schedule I had set for myself. Then before I knew it the words, "Absolutely I do!," came rolling off my tongue. She explained that she would have to make it a working trip but at least we were going to Florida. That was fine with me as I had to continue to write if I was to meet my deadline.

After spending the night in Birmingham, we arrived late Wednesday afternoon in time to unpack and change to go hear her friend that night. Our plan was to stay over Thursday night and drive home Friday. We awoke the next morning to clouds and a possible chance of rain. I began to pray that the Lord would be gracious and allow the sun to shine on this our only day to see the beach. Before I began to write that morning, I decided to go for a walk. Did I mention that this was January? Even in Florida, January can be a little chilly!

As I began to walk, the sun was trying with all its might to burst forth through the low cloud cover. The closer I got to the beach the more intense the sunlight seemed to become. I noticed quite a few people walking on the beach, so I decided to join them. I walked for forty minutes before laying my t-shirt on the sand to sit awhile. God's creation was absolutely amazing and invigorating! The white caps on the waves seemed to be forcefully making their way to shore as the rays of sunshine shimmered and reflected off the water. I found myself worshipping God right in the midst of those walking along the beach that morning.

Busyness causes our bow and our lives to be strung tightly, robbing us of rest, solitude, quiet, and peace. I was completely rested and rejuvenated from my time of solitude that morning. Do you need to lay your "busy" aside for a little rest, solitude, quiet, and peace?

Come with me by yourselves to a quiet place.
You need to get some rest.
Mark 6:31 NIRV

---

[45]Donald S. Whitney, *Spiritual Disciplines for the Christian Life* (Colorado Springs, Colorado: Nav Press, 1991). P. 190

Day One

There is a new buzz word floating around out there and that word is **busy**. I often hear women say, "I am just busy, busy, busy." It is proclaimed as if it were a great trophy to hoist into the air and show everyone. But perhaps, it is not a trophy that we should be boasting about. **Busy** does not always mean productive!

1. If someone were to ask you to define the word **busy**, what would you say? Write your answer below.

2. List a few synonyms for the word **busy**.

One of the synonyms I found was "working at." Who wants more work? Why would we choose to do something that requires us to work more, sleep less, and cost us spiritually, emotionally, and physically?

Webster's Dictionary defines **busy** as *engaged in action, full of activity, and full of distracting detail*. In contrast let's look at the word **rest** which is an antonym (a word that is the opposite of another word) for **busy**. The word **rest** appears many times in the Bible.

3. How would you define the word **rest**?

The Webster's Dictionary defines **rest** as *ceasing to work or move in order to relax, refresh oneself, or recover strength*.

Rest is a necessity. It is a Biblical principle that all of God's creation must **rest**—why do you think they call it winter rest? Winter rest being a state of reduced activity for plants and animals alike. Without proper rest the human body will wear down. The word **rest** is found 585 times in the Amplified Bible and 540 in the New King James Version, so obviously, this is an important principle God wants us to learn. Even God himself saw the need to rest.

> *And on the seventh day God finished his work that he had done, and he **rested** on the seventh day from all his work that he had done. So God blessed the seventh day and made it holy, because on it God **rested** from all his work that he had done in creation. Genesis 2:2-3 ESV*

> *Rest has never been one of Americans greatest strengths. According to one study, only one in seven adults (14%) have set aside an entire day for the purpose of rest. For those who do set aside an entire day, can you guess how they fill their time? Mostly with work. Over 40% say they do enjoyable work, and an additional 37% say they will do non-enjoyable work, if it has to get done (Raking leaves anyone?). Out of the 14% who set aside a day of rest, only 19% say they won't work at all on their day of rest.[46]*
> *—Stuart R Strachan Jr.*

4. When your calendar is full and you have committed to too many things, explain below how this makes you feel emotionally, spiritually, and physically? What are the results of over commitment in each of these areas?

EMOTIONALLY:

SPIRITUALLY:

PHYSICALLY:

[46]Stuart R. Strachan Jr., https://thepastorsworkshop.com/sermon-illustrations-on-rest

The world, and yes, even the church, can keep us busy—there are always things to be done. I was talking to a young lady who said she received a text from a friend at her church asking her to do an in-depth Bible study with a group of women. The young lady began her response with, "I might be able to do that." She felt pressure after all, it was a Bible study. Then she proceeded to list what she was committed to at the time. It went something like this, "I am currently homeschooling our youngest who struggles with a learning issue, I am involved in her tutoring one day a week, then I am discipling a young lady using the Chronological Bible. Our family is going through a devotional series called *Foundations* and my husband and I are helping with a small group at church, which meets every other week."

She said when she finished texting, she realized she did not need one more thing to do, even a good thing such as a Bible study. So, she began erasing her list and responded with, "Thank you for asking, but I cannot commit to the Bible study at this time in my life."

Busy, although not a word with totally negative connotations, can often lead to negative results. If this young lady had said yes to the **one more** thing, although a good thing, there would have been negative results.

Busyness and over commitment is a **distraction** in our lives. My husband used to say, "God is not concerned with our doing, but our being." We cannot **be** in Him, what He desires us to **be**, when we are so **busy** that we have no time for Him.

5. If you were asked to define the state of "being" from God's perspective, how would you define it?

Let me be clear, I am not criticizing church commitments. I believe it is biblical to serve. I believe it is biblical to corporately study God's Word. But, it is not biblical to be so **busy** that we lack the time to rest, sacrifice relationships, miss personal time in God's Word and prayer, and miss hearing God speak into our lives.

6. Write Matthew 11:28.

Busyness wearies us, but God can restore us if we will choose to slow down and find rest in Him. We make a choice daily, weekly, monthly, and yearly as to how **busy** we will be. In the days to come, we will look at the results of choosing **busy** versus choosing to allow God to set our calendar and commitments.

PONDER:

I wanted to figure out why I was so busy, but I couldn't find the time to do it.[47]
—Todd Stocker

MEDITATE:

Six days you will do all your work. But the seventh day is a Day of Rest to the Lord your God.
You, your son, your daughter, your male servant, your female servant, your cattle,
or the traveler who stays with you, must not do any work on this day.
Exodus 20:10 NLV

PRAY:

Lord, I've done it again! I am guilty of saying yes to everyone else and thus living
a life of **busyness** *and preoccupation, which often leads to weariness! I overload my calendar*
in order to please others instead of desiring to please You. Teach me to daily set myself apart
in order to receive my directives from You. I need to be still, sitting in Your presence,
listening and learning. You are the One who brings rest and order into my life.
Amen!

[47]Todd Stocker, www.goodreads.com/busy

Day Two

Like many of you who have experienced flight delays while traveling, I had a flight delay in Dallas. Since the delay was going to be several hours, I decided to walk. As I walked from one corridor to another I began to notice that people were busy on their iPhones, laptops, and computers. Not one person was taking a nap or sitting having a long conversation with the person to their right or left. They were all **plugged in**. Even those sitting in a restaurant or coffee bar were **plugged in**. Before all of the technology, people traveling could disconnect from their busy lives for a while. While traveling, the only way they could be reached by their family in an emergency was through calling the main airport phone lines.

Not that many years ago, when you left on vacation, your job did not go with you. When you went on your honeymoon—your family did not go with you. Your overloaded calendar and commitments were left behind—you could **unplug** from life and enjoy yourself. Now, every aspect of your life—stress and all goes with you wherever you go and all because of a few plugs!

1. Is being **plugged in** adding stress and a spirit of weariness to your life? In what ways?

In Kevin DeYoung's book, *Crazy Busy*, he wrote, "I read an anecdote once about a woman from another culture who came to the United States and began to introduce herself as 'Busy.' It was, after all, the first thing she heard when meeting any American. 'Hello, I'm Busy'—she figured it was part of our traditional greeting, so she told everyone she met that that's who she was."[48]

This is a sad commentary on the United States! I think we as Americans are addicted to **busy**. I don't think it is just an American problem, but I do believe it is more prevalent in the United States than in other countries around the world. We look at **busy** as being a good thing, a sign of success, a badge of honor, a way to avoid dealing with life, and as a way of keeping up with everyone around us.

In Day One, we saw that busyness can cause weariness. But if we will slow down and concentrate on our "being" instead of our "doing," God promises **peace** and **rest**. God is the ultimate source of both.

2. Fill in the missing words from John 14:27: "_____ _____ I leave with you. My _____ I give to you. I do not give to you as the world gives. Your _____ must not be _____ or fearful" (HCBS).

Busyness is not God's idea—but man's idea.

If you are ...

- Caught up in pleasing others

 [48]Kevin De Young, *Crazy Busy*, https://www.goodreads.com/work/quotes/23572309-crazy-busy-a-mercifully-short-book

- Saying YES to everything you are asked to do

- Chasing dreams or the dream job

- Feeling pressure to conform

- Signing your kids up for numerous extracurricular activities because your friend's children are signed up—this is not from God!

3. Read Mark 6:30-32. What did Jesus admonish His disciples to do?

Jesus' days of ministry were **busy**. But He knew the value of **unplugging** from ministry and setting aside time to rest.

> *A native Hawaiian once told me the origin of the name that islanders use for us non-Hawaiians—haole. Haole is a Hawaiian word for 'no breath.' The name became associated with the European immigrants of the 1820's. While there are varying explanations for this term, I like the one he gave me: 'Our forefathers thought the settlers were always in a hurry to build plantations, harbors, and ranches. To the native Hawaiians they seemed short of breath.'* [49]
> —*Max Lucado*

Are you short of breath? Perhaps you need to **unplug** from the busyness of life and pursue the God of rest, allowing Him to renew, refresh, and restore you.

4. What are some practical ways you can begin to **unplug** from busyness?

We as Christians don't want to just survive this busy life, we want to thrive in this life. In order to thrive we must unplug from the busy and purposely pursue the only true source of peace, joy, and contentment—God.

[49]Max Lucado, *Anxious for Nothing* (Nashville, Tennessee: Thomas Nelson, 2017).
https://thepastorsworkshop.com/sermon-illustrations-on-busyness

5. Write the definition of the word **deliberately**.

We must consciously **unplug** from busyness and **deliberately** pursue the Prince of Peace, if we want to thrive instead of survive in this life. His will for us is to thrive—not just survive!

PONDER:

We often become mentally and spiritually barren because we are so busy.[50]
—Franklin Graham

MEDITATE:

Look carefully then how you walk, not as unwise but as wise, making the best use of the time, because the days are evil. Therefore do not be foolish, but understand what the will of the Lord is.
Ephesians 5:15-17 ESV

PRAY:

Father, I know Your heart is broken when I choose "doing" over "being."
Help me to be discerning in committing my time and energy. Show me the intention of my heart when devoting my time to activities. My desire is to be in deliberate pursuit of You over pleasing man or my flesh. Help me to walk as wise and not as unwise.
Amen!

[50]Franklin, Graham, https://www.azquotes.com/quote/1415204

Day Three

For the past several years, since our grandchildren who live locally were small, they have taken turns spending the night once a month. The menu for the night usually consist of pizza and a trip to *Menchies Yogurt*. The toppings on the pizza are a much easier decision than what type of yogurt and toppings they will have. There are so many **choices**! I stopped trying to add up the hours I have spent waiting for them to try every flavor of yogurt and then decide which three special toppings they will **choose**.

We wake up to **choices** every day, and we can **choose**:

- What we will eat for breakfast

- What we will wear for the day

- What time we will leave for work based on the traffic report

- What time we will go to bed that night—just to name a few

Years ago, I had a young lady from South America come to my class. She had only been in the United States a few months. I asked her what her biggest adjustment had been. She answered, "The grocery store." I asked, "What is it about the grocery store that has been an adjustment?" She responded, "There are too **many choices**. It overwhelms me."

At times, the **choices** we have to make can seem overwhelming. The word **choose** means *to decide on a course of action*. We look at all of our **choices** and then we **choose** what will be best for us and how we will accomplish it without allowing it to overwhelm us.

God gave every man and woman a free will. With that free will we have the "freedom" to make choices—to **choose**.

1. Read Ruth Chapters 1-4.

2. What choice was Ruth given?

3. Was her choice a good one or a bad one? Explain.

4. What was the result of Ruth's choice to stay with Naomi?

Ruth could choose to either stay in her home country or trust Naomi's God and go with her mother-in-law. She made a wise **choice** and God blessed her. She benefitted from that **choice** and so did Naomi!

When it comes to commitments, we can **choose**:

- Just how full our calendar will be

- Whether we want to please Christ or people

- To say Yes just because saying NO is harder

- Busyness with all of its consequences

- To say NO because it is the wisest choice for us

- To restrain from over commitment which will require discipline

We must discipline our lives, but we must do so all the year round, and not merely at stated periods. I must discipline myself at all times.[51]
— Martyn Lloyd-Jones

Saying "Yes" to commitments is often easy, while saying "No" is hard and requires restraint and discipline.

5. Write 2 Timothy 1:7 (NASB) below.

[51]https://www.goodreads.com/book/show/202206.Studies_in_the_Sermon_on_the_Mo

Paul tells Timothy, "Don't be fearful and timid, for that spirit is not from God. Be loving, strong, and disciplined."

We need the rugged strength of Christian character that can come from discipline.[52]
—*V. Raymond Edman*

We must exercise discipline and a rugged strength of character in limiting our commitments, placing margins in our calendars, and saying NO when saying YES would be easier.

PONDER:

No is a small word but it is harder to say than Yes!
—Author Unknown

MEDITATE:

Then choose for yourselves right now whom you will serve.
Joshua 24:15a

PRAY:

Father, saying NO to others is hard for me. My best yes is when I say yes to You.
Help me to place You above commitments and pleasing people. Give me the strength to resist
overloading my calendar and help me to develop the discipline of restraint in making choices.
Amen!

[52]Quoted in: Donald S. Whitney, *Spiritual Disciplines for the Christian Life* (Colorado Springs, Colorado: Nav Press, 1991). P.15

Day Four

I remember the first time I heard the expression **FOMO** it was in listening to a message by a pastor in Atlanta, Georgia. I had never heard of the "Fear of Missing Out." As many of you know, the term is used in relationship to social media and its effect on people. I looked up the definition of **FOMO**. Can you believe this new word has actually made it into the dictionary? It is defined as *a pervasive apprehension that others might be having rewarding experiences from which one is absent*—the one being you and me!

As I was writing this lesson, the word **FOMO** came to mind. At the time, I was contemplating all the reasons we commit to so many activities—overloading our lives and calendars. I believe the reason is that we have a pervasive apprehension that others might be having rewarding experiences from which we are absent. Therefore, we must do everything they are doing in order to be "happy" and "fulfilled." No one wants to be left out, right?

1. So, let me ask you, are you suffering with activity commitment **FOMO**? Yes or No. Explain.

> *The weapons of faith in God and love for His Word*
> *will free you from the self-imposed prison of fear.*
> *—Author Unknown*

2. What is the root of **FOMO**?

The root of **FOMO** is the same root we find with any type of insecurity: Satan himself! Remember our verse from 2 Timothy 1:7? "God does not give us a spirit of fear (anxiety) or timidity (lacking self-confidence)."

If Satan can occupy our minds with feelings of insecurity (anxiety and uncertainty), and a fear of being left out, then he can lead us right into over commitment and busyness. The over commitment will be a **distraction** that draws us away from our devotion to Christ—that is a high price to pay not to be socially left out. Satan loves to **distract** us through any means he can—**FOMO** included.

> *If the enemy can distract you from your time alone with God, then he can isolate you from the help that comes from God alone. —Author Unknown*

3. Are you over committed? What is your busyness costing you spiritually?

4. What is your busyness costing you personally/relationally?

When those closest to us have stopped asking for our time, it's because they know we are too busy for them. That's crushing to the heart.[53] *—Tammy Whitehurst*

Many of us are so incredibly busy filling up our calendars with meaningless activities that we often miss out on loving and ministering to others. We must ask if we are investing our time wisely? There are numerous examples of those in the Bible who invested wisely and took the time to minister to others. Let's read about a couple.

Read Exodus 18:13-27.

---

[53]Tammy Whitehurst, Article: *Busyness is Not a Spiritual Gift*, www.christianitytoday.com

Jethro, Moses's father-in-law, was visiting. He took the time to observe the staggering load Moses was carrying in leading God's people and help him find a solution.

5. What advice did Jethro give Moses and how was it helpful in relieving some of the pressure that was upon Moses?

Read Acts 9:32-42.

Peter ministered in Judea. He took time to visit the believers in the town of Lydda and Joppa.

6. Who were those who benefited from Peter's willingness to take time to minister in Lydda and Joppa? How did each benefit?

> *None of us can help everyone. But all of us can help someone. And when we help them,*
> *we serve Jesus. Who would want to miss a chance to do that?*[54]
> —*Max Lucado*

Jesus and His disciples were busy with their ministry, but never too busy to stop and take the time to love, help, heal, and encourage people. They never missed a chance and neither should we!

7. Aren't we to be imitators of Christ? Aren't we to be His disciples in our city, community, and on the earth? Write Ephesians 5:1-2 below.

 [54]Max Lucado, www.wow4us.com/max-lucado-quotes

If we are filling our lives with too many commitments due to **FOMO**, we cannot be imitators of God, His children, His disciples, and His representatives—loving and ministering as He did. If our calendars and lives are busy, busy, busy, and we have not left margins, we cannot be a sacrifice and an offering of love as He was for many. In our busyness, we will fail to be a fragrant aroma to the world around us as Jethro, Peter, Jesus, and the disciples were!

PONDER:

A man who wants to lead the orchestra must turn his back on the crowd.[55]
—Max Lucado

MEDITATE:

Do nothing from selfish ambition or conceit, but in humility regard others as better than yourselves. Let each of you look not to your own interests, but to the interests of others. Let the same mind be in you that was in Christ Jesus. Philippians 2:3-5 NRSV

PRAY:

Father, I know that when I struggle with a pervasive apprehension that others might be having rewarding experiences from which I am absent, those thoughts and feelings of insecurity come from Satan. Guard my mind and give me a sacrificial heart that desires to meet the needs of others. Help me to leave margins in my calendar so that I am free to follow Your Spirit's leading in loving and serving others. Amen!

[55]Max Lucado, www.smartandrelentless.com

Day Five

Have you ever heard the phrase "Go With the Flow?" There are t-shirts, sweatshirts, mugs, and bumper stickers, all encouraging us to follow the flow of the world. Now, what about the phrase "Go Against the Flow?" This phrase is not as popular. It specifically encourages Christians not to follow the flow of the world. While much of the world is swimming in one direction, we are admonished to swim in the opposite direction.

In Week One we looked at Romans 12:2. In the New Living Translation it reads, "Don't copy the behavior and customs of this world."

In other words, whatever the world (your friends) are doing, you don't have to do the same. God has different plans for each of us. He encourages us to "Go Against the Flow" because His plan for each of us is a personal plan.

1. Fill in the blanks for Philippians 29:11: "For _____ _____ the plans _____ have for you," says the _____. "They are plans for good and not for disaster, to give you a _____ and a _____" (NLT).

Going against the flow is difficult simply because it sets us apart from everyone else.

Mark was radically saved in April of 1984, and I was saved that June. Over the fourth of July, that summer, we planned a trip to see family and friends in Nashville. While we were there we wanted to have dinner with a couple that had been our friends since college. We were so excited to tell them about our recent commitment to Christ and the difference it had made in our lives, home, and family. This couple, like us, had grown up going to church. After Mark and I finished sharing with them, the husband looked at us and said, "We may not be able to be friends any longer." And we weren't! Unbeknownst to us, we had offended them and made them feel as if we were saying they were not saved. But, we were not saying that at all. At that point, we headed down different paths—set apart by what God had chosen for Mark and me.

If you have ever had an idea or wanted to make a change that went **against** what everyone around you was thinking or doing, you know it does not always go well. Or if you have ever felt the need to resist going in a direction everyone else was taking, this decision or choice might have cost you a few relationships. That is exactly what happened with our Nashville friends.

2. Write Psalm 25:12 below.

When you consult God as to the "way" you are to go, the commitments you are or are not to choose, He promises to show you—but it might be different from everyone around you.

> *God's call for us as His children is to separate ourselves*
> *from the world, to come out from them (2 Corinthians 6:17).*
> —*Author Unknown*

When God calls you to "come out from them," that is what we are referring to in saying, "Go Against the Flow."

Over the years of Mark's illness, we had a young couple offer us their lake home as a getaway. We accepted and I have wonderful memories from our time there. Mark and I would often sit on the deck observing the tugboats, barges, sail boats, and fishermen on the lake. One thing that was obvious was the flow of the current each day. The speed at which each was able to travel was dependent upon whether or not it was going **with** the current or **against** the current. Obviously, going **against** the current was much harder than going **with** the current.

- It is the same for us in choosing to say NO to busyness when everyone else is choosing to say YES—you will be going **against** the current.

- In saying NO, we have to go **against** the current and this can be hard for us to do.

Many of your friends can appear to have it all together in their busyness thus causing you to think that busy is okay.

But, did you know that bodies of water that look calm on the surface can often have a fast under current? That's dangerous enough alone, but add boulders, logs, and other debris (**more commitments**) and injury becomes likely.

According to the CDC, drowning is the fifth leading cause of unintentional injury and death in the United States. Your friends may look calm on the surface of their choosing busyness but all the while they and their families may be drowning!

> **Distractions** *can be a threat to the Christian's maturing life in Christ.*

Busyness is a distraction! It is a current that pulls us away from seeking devotion with our Creator.

TRUE CONFESSION:

I am guilty, as many of you are, of being distracted by busyness.

I know there are opportunities to be a blessing to others that I am missing due to my busyness. When I finish explaining my exhaustive list, in talking with others, they immediately apologize for taking my "valuable" time. That is wrong on my part! After all, I made the choice to be busy. I should not talk so much about what I am doing that people then feel guilty for taking up my time. Those conversations are all about me—not them. Busyness robs us of tuning in to the needs of others and being able to minister to them as God would have us do.

Two things I am trying to be more disciplined in:

#1 is not talking about all that I am doing.

#2 is trying to leave margins in my schedule so God can use me to be a blessing to others.

You and I have a **choice** when it comes to busyness, so, what if we ...

- Chose **rest** over busy

- Chose to **unplug** from the pressure to conform to the world around us

- Chose to say **NO** to what everyone else is doing just because they are doing it

- Chose **Christ** over a preoccupation with busyness

- Chose **margin** over a full calendar

- Chose to not allow **FOMO** to define us and our commitments

3. What good results would occur as a result of making the above choices?

4. If you have chosen to **go against the flow**, what are some blessings you can see God pouring out as a result of your **choice**?

PONDER:

People are watching the way we act more than they are listening to what we say.[56]
—Max Lucado

MEDITATE:

I say this to you: Let the Holy Spirit lead you in each step.
Then you will not please your sinful old selves.
Galatians 5:16 NLV

PRAY:

Lord, the world pulls so hard on me to overcommit. Often, I am swept into
the current of busyness. I don't wat to copy the behavior and customs of this world.
I want to be set apart for Your heavenly good. Help me to seek Your direction in making
commitments for You know the plans You have for me. May I have the strength to
go against the flow and follow You will for my life, pleasing You and You alone.
Amen!

[56]Max Lucado, www.goodreads.com/author/quotes/2737.Max_Lucado

Week Four Menu

Santa Fe Taco Soup

1 small onion, diced

1 tablespoon olive oil

1 pound ground beef or 1 pound
cooked chicken breast, cubed

2 (15 ounce) cans white corn

1 (15 ounce) can diced tomatoes

1 (15 ounce) can Rotel

1 (15 ounce) can navy beans

1 (5 ounce) can pinto beans

1 (15 ounce) can black beans

2 (1 ounce) packets taco seasoning

2 (1 ounce) packets Hidden Valley Ranch dressing

1½ cups water

Top with:

1 cup Cheddar cheese, grated

Tortilla chips

In saucepan over medium heat, sauté onion in one tablespoon olive oil until tender. Add ground beef and brown. Drain. (Cubed chicken can be substituted). Place in *Crock-Pot*. Add remaining ingredients. Do not drain cans. Cook for one hour on low and 30 minutes on high. Serve with tortilla chips and grated Cheddar cheese. Note: It is recommended that you not drain beans. If you desire to drain and rinse beans, add 1 to 2 cups beef or chicken broth in place of juices.

Homemade Hidden Valley Ranch Mix

½ cup dry buttermilk powder

1 tablespoon dried parsley for blending

1 teaspoon reserved

1 teaspoon dried dill weed for blending

½ teaspoon reserved

1 teaspoon onion powder

1 teaspoon dried onion flakes (or dried chopped onion)

1 teaspoon salt

1 teaspoon garlic powder

2 tablespoons organic dried portabella
pieces mushrooms (in produce section)

1 teaspoon garlic salt

¼ teaspoon ground pepper

½ teaspoon sugar

Add all the dry ingredients except the reserved teaspoon of dried parsley and the ½ teaspoon of dried dill to your blender. Blend until a nice powder. Hand mix in the reserved parsley and dill (you want to see some herbs in your mix). Store dry mix in an air-tight container or jar in your pantry for 2 to 3 months or in the freezer for 6 months or longer. Note: Use 2 tablespoons of dry mix in any recipe asking for dry ranch mix. **To make Hidden Valley Ranch Dip**: Mix 2 tablespoons of dry mix with ½ to 1 cup of sour cream. Chill for 2 hours and serve as a dip. **To make Hidden Valley Ranch Dressing for Salads**: Mix together 3 tablespoons Dry Ranch Dip mix, 1 cup of mayonnaise and 2/3 cup buttermilk. Mix together and chill in the refrigerator for 1 to 2 hours. Serve and enjoy! Note: Makes large amount. Mushrooms can be difficult to find, check with grocer.

Homemade Taco Seasoning

1 part chili powder

1 part ground cumin

1 part garlic powder

1 part onion powder

¼ –½ parts crushed red pepper

Mix all the spices together and store in an airtight container. Can be stored in the freezer. Use sparingly, or liberally!

Joy's Mexican Cornbread

2 cups self-rising cornmeal

1 cup self-rising flour

½ pint sour cream

2 eggs, room temperature

1 (14 ounce) can whole kernel corn (with liquid)

1 small onion, chopped

1 medium green pepper, chopped

1 jalapeño, seeded and diced

Preheat oven to 400°F. In mixing bowl, combine all dry ingredients. Stir in sour cream, eggs, corn, onion, green pepper, and jalapeño pepper until incorporated. Pour batter into hot greased skillet and bake for 30 to 40 minutes until golden brown.

Old-Fashioned Banana Pudding

¼ cup plus 2 tablespoons all-purpose flour

1 cup sugar

⅛ teaspoon salt

1 cup milk

1 cup half and half

2 large eggs, lightly beaten

¼ cup butter

2 teaspoons vanilla

36 vanilla wafers

3 ripe bananas

Fresh whipped cream

Combine flour, sugar and salt in a medium saucepan; stir in milk, half and half, and eggs. Cook over medium heat, stirring constantly, until mixture thickens. Add butter and vanilla, and cook, stirring constantly until butter melts. Remove from heat. Cool. Layer vanilla wafers and bananas evenly into 6 individual dessert dishes, spoon pudding on top and repeat layer. Top with fresh whipped cream. Note: Crushed Nutter Butter cookies can be substituted for vanilla wafers.

FRESH WHIPPED CREAM:

2 cups heavy whipping cream

2 tablespoons confectioners' sugar

2 teaspoons vanilla

In mixing bowl on low, mix heavy cream, confectioners' sugar, and vanilla. Once mixed thoroughly, increase speed to medium and whip for 5 minutes, then increase to high until cream is spreading consistency. Note: Do not over mix; will become butter!

SHORT-CUTS...

- **SANTA FE TACO SOUP:** Make soup earlier in the day, turn off after cooking time. An hour before dinner, warm in *Crock-Pot*.

- **JOY'S MEXICAN CORNBREAD:** Make cornbread ahead and re-heat or serve room temperature.

- **OLD-FASHIONED BANANA PUDDING:** If making banana pudding the morning you are serving and placing in refrigerate, you may want to soak banana slices in a little lemon juice for 5 minutes to keep from browning. If you are worried about the flavor changing, stick to the sweeter, lighter flavors: Lemon juice, Orange juice, Tinned pineapple juice, Tinned or fresh grapefruit juice, Lime juice and Apple juice. Bananas should be fine if pudding is made in the morning and served the same day. <u>Note</u>: Use critic juice or drink to prevent discoloration of bananas.

HEALTHY TIPS...

- **SANTA FE TACO SOUP:** Roast your own chicken. Use organic chicken or grass-fed beef.

- **SANTA FE TACO SOUP:** To avoid MSG and other additives, make homemade seasonings instead of using seasoning packets. Recipes provided.

- **SANTA FE TACO SOUP:** Use fresh, frozen or organic corn in place of can corn. These are healthier choices. Many processed canned foods have preservatives added.

- **SANTA FE TACO SOUP:** Corn is best and sweetest cooked in the husk. Pull back the husk and remove the silk, replace the husk, tie them together at the top with string. Cook as you would husk corn, even when boiling. When grilling, soak in cold water for 15 minutes so that the husks don't burn while grilling. **Alternative:** Microwave 4 to 5 minutes before grilling to greatly reduce cooking time on the grill. Remove kernels by cutting a small piece off the tip of cob to make it flat. Holding stem edge, stand the corn upright with flat end on a cutting board. Use a firm-bladed sharp knife and cut downward removing the corn.

- **SANTA FE TACO SOUP:** Use organic beans, drained and add ½- 1 cup organic beef broth to replace drained off bean juice.

- **SANTA FE TACO SOUP:** Substitute *Marca El Pato Salsa de Jalapeno* for the Rotel. It has all natural ingredients and no additives. Found at local grocery.

- **USE BAKED TORTILLA CHIPS OR MAKE YOUR OWN:** Lightly spray tortillas with olive oil cooking spray and season with salt, pepper, and/or chili powder. Cut each into 12 wedges and bake at 350°F until crisp. Homemade are lower in salt and preservatives.

- **CORNBREAD AND PUDDING:** For today's cornbread and pudding recipes, use unbleached all-purpose flour.

Finances

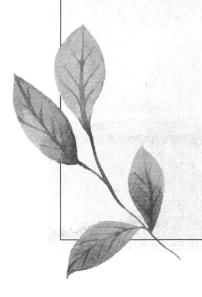

Does your use of money—that which you exchange so much of your life for—make clear that you are following Christ and pursuing godliness?
—Donald S. Whitney

When the pastor announces that he will be preaching an upcoming series on money, the attendance immediately drops! People don't want to be told what to do with **their** money. The problem is that as Christians—it is not **our** money! There was a sweet little elderly woman in the Bible who understood this biblical principle. We meet her in the book of Mark. This woman was unassuming, quiet, gentle, and a widow. On the day we meet her, she is entering the Temple where Jesus was teaching. After teaching, as he sat to rest, he observed those who were bringing their offerings. Mark says, "Then a poor widow came and dropped in two small coins." Now this got the attention of Jesus. This was a great visual and teaching tool for Him to use with his disciples. So, He called them over (Mark 12:41:44 NLT).

Thinking of my dad, I had to chuckle when I read this story. Being a college professor, he never missed an opportunity to turn a "life experience" into a "life lesson." Jesus did just that with his guys and said, "I tell you the truth, this poor widow has given more than all the others who are making contributions. For they gave a tiny part of their surplus, but she, poor as she is, has given everything she had to live on." His disciples had to be thinking, "That does not make sense. The rich people have given large amounts. How can this widow with her two small coins have given more?" They missed what we often miss; the rich gave **some** of their wealth, while she gave **all** she had. Chances are the rich gave out of their "abundance." Jesus called it their "surplus." But, she gave the last two coins she had. She sacrificed in faith and out of devotion to the Lord. The rich were distracted by their abundance and gave what they did not need.

When it comes to your money, are you more like the rich people or the widow? Do you give sacrificially in faith and out of devotion to the Lord trusting that He will take care of you? Or, are you distracted by your abundance and give because you really do not need what you have given?

> *The proportion of your income that you give back to God is one distinctive indication*
> *of how much you trust Him to provide for your needs.*[57]
> —*Donald S. Whitney*

Like many of the issues Christians face, money is a **heart** issue. The widow's **heart** was devoted to the Lord; therefore, her money was devoted to the Lord. Jesus in teaching about money and possessions in the book of Matthew said, "Wherever your treasure is, there the desires of your **heart** will also be ... No one can serve two masters. For you will hate one and love the other; you will be devoted to one and despise the other. You cannot serve God and be enslaved to money" (Matthew 6:21-24 NLT).

It is easier for many church members to stay home when the pastor preaches a series on money. In that way, they don't have to face the issue of selfishness within their own **hearts**. But, one day we will enter the Temple of heaven where God has been seated observing our lives and our giving, and we will have to provide an account of what we did with **His** money that **He** so graciously entrusted to us.

Will your giving be a life lesson for others or an example of one who gave out of her surplus?

---

[57]Donald S. Whitney, *Spiritual Disciplines for the Christian Life* (Colorado Springs, Colorado: NavPress, 1991). P. 143

Day One

Just a short flick of the wrist and a move of our curser, and voila, millions of products are available for us to purchase—and all from our cozy den chair! We can go to Amazon for just about anything, Wayfair for furniture, rugs, and house decorations, Zulily for a new dress, or Zappos for a fabulous new pair of shoes! As if that's not enough, just about any of our favorite stores offer us on-line shopping.

I see two problems with this new phenomenon: First, it is too easy to go into debt. Secondly, it is a **distraction** in our lives. We spend hours feeding our **want** monster and the spirit of discontentment by scrolling from one option for purchasing to another. It is almost effortless. We just start by finding what we **want**, then dropping it in our cart, proceeding to checkout where our card number automatically pops up, we approve the sale and it is ours! And as incredible as it seems, it will be on our doorstep the following day! We never even had to get dressed or leave our cozy den chair. Amazing!

You can't buy discipline, but you have an inner ability to develop self-control.
—Author Unknown

Lack of self-control in spending your monies, whether in an actual store or through on-line means can be both **destructive** and **distracting**. It is **destructive** in that it can wreak havoc with your budget, and **distracting**, in that it draws your affections toward *things* rather than Christ.

1. Fill in the blanks of the following verse: "He who _____ _____ will never have _____ _____ to make him happy. It is the same for the one who _____ to get many _____. This also is for nothing (Ecclesiastes 5:10 NLV).

2. Does this verse bring about conviction in your **heart** or an attitude of "my money is my own business?" As you read this verse, if you found yourself thinking "my money is my own business," confess this wrong attitude to the Lord. Remember all we have as Christians is His! He owns it all!

3. Fill in the blank: "The earth is the _____, and all that is in it, the world, and all who live in it" (Psalm 24:1 NLV).

4. Does money and the possession of **things** hold first place in your **heart**? Check the appropriate answer. Be honest. **Yes**_____ **No**_____ **More times than not**_____

If your answer to the question was "Yes" or "More Times Than Not," prayerfully ask the Lord to turn the affection of your **heart** away from money and things and back to Him.

Let's read a story about a man whose **heart** was given to **money** and the possession of things.

Read God's instructions in Joshua 6:18-19 and the people's response in Joshua chapter 7.

God had given the children of Israel victory at Jericho. He also gave them specific instructions related to the plunder obtained from the city upon destruction. Now they were coming up against another enemy. Joshua sent out a group of spies to spy on the people of Ai. Believing the report of the spies, he sends an army of 3000 out to fight and they are defeated. Joshua's prayer questions God as to why He **allowed** this defeat.

5.   Read Joshua 7:10-13. How did God respond to Joshua?

6.   What did God say was the reason He had removed His hand of protection from them?

Achan was **distracted** by the silver coins, bars of gold, and the beautiful robes he discovered upon attacking and plundering Jericho. His **love** of **money** and things robbed him of his devotion to God and his desire to obey God's Word.

7.   What was the result of Achan's disobedience? (Joshua 7:19-25)

Achan was guilty of false thinking.

- He falsely thought his sin could be hidden from God.

- He falsely thought his sin would not affect others—but it cost many their lives.

- He falsely thought he deserved to have the silver, gold, and ornamental robes.

- He falsely thought things held a greater value than his relationship with God.

Achan's affection was drawn away by the allure of wealth. That affection cost him his life and it cost the lives of those he loved—his family. Where have you set your affection?

8. Is your devotion to the Lord being affected by your **love** of **money** and things? Explain the ways it is being affected.

Achan's **heart** was the opposite of the widow found in the book of Mark. Remember what Matthew said, "Wherever your treasure is, there the **desires** of your **heart** will also be ... No one can serve two masters" (Matthew 6:21, 24 NLT). His **heart** was devoted to money and possession; he wanted to hold onto it all. The widow was willing to let go of all she had in devotion to her Lord.

He who lays up treasures on earth spends his life backing away from his treasures. To him, death is loss. He who lays up treasures in heaven looks forward to eternity; he's moving daily toward his treasures. To him, death is gain. He who spends his life moving toward his treasures has reason to rejoice. Are you despairing or rejoicing? [58]
—Randy Alcorn

PONDER:

If I love money more than Christ, woe is me! [59]
—William Tiptaft

MEDITATE:

It is better to be godly and have little than to be evil and rich.
For the strength of the wicked will be shattered, but the Lord takes care of the godly.
Psalm 37:16-17 NLT

PRAY:

Sweet Father, nothing is hidden from You. I don't want my money or
my possessions to distract me, define me, or steal away my devotion to You.
Forgive me for setting my heart on things rather than You.
The desire of my heart is to find my satisfaction in You, Father.
I am so thankful that You, Lord, are always enough!
Amen!

[58]Randy Alcorn, https://www.christianquotes.info/quotes-by-author/randy-alcorn-quotes
[59]https://www.whatchristianswanttoknow.com/22-christian-quotes-about-money/#ixzz6ntlans1N

Day Two

Around Valentine's Day each year, we see hearts of every shape, size, and design. The emphasis of this holiday is on the **heart** and the devotion of our hearts—to the ones in our lives that we love. There are a multitude of choices when it comes to hearts—white chocolate, milk chocolate, dark chocolate, and sweet tart hearts, just to name a few. So what type of **heart** would the one you love cherish on Valentine's Day?

When the Bible speaks of the **heart**, there are many different hearts mentioned. We see the selfish heart, the generous heart, the obedient heart, the sinful heart, the wicked heart, the happy heart, and the divided heart.

1. What type of **heart** would the Father, who loves you so much, cherish in you? Choose from the list above.

2. How would you define the word **emulate**?

3. Whose **heart** do these types of hearts **emulate**?

God is serious about the hearts of His children. If we are truly His, our **heart** will emulate, (imitate or copy) His **heart**. Having a **heart** of generosity, obedience, and cheerfulness (happiness) reflects the **heart** of God.

We see another aspect of God's heart in Genesis 6:6. Read the verse below.

"So the Lord was sorry he had ever made them and put them on the earth. It **broke** his heart" (NLT).

- God's **heart** was broken over the sin within Eve and Adam's hearts.

- A sinful, disobedient, divided, wicked, and selfish **heart** breaks the Father's heart.

113

4. Write the definition of the word **selfish**.

Having a selfish **heart**, lacking compassion and consideration for others, is the very opposite of God's character. According to Ephesians 5:1 (ESV), we as Christians are to be _____ of Christ. Having a selfish **heart** is not emulating or imitating Christ.

Generosity is not measured by how much we give away. Generosity is measured by how much we keep for ourselves.
—*Author Unknown*

So far in our studies, Achan suffered with a selfish **heart** keeping the spoils for himself. But, the widow emulated the heart of God. She gave all she had. Her heart was generous, as God's **heart** is generous.

5. Write the definition of the word **generous**.

6. What does Proverbs 4:23 (NIV) say about our **hearts**? Fill in the following blanks: "Above all else, _____ your _____, for everything you do _____ from it."

7. When it comes to our money and possessions, how can we guard our **hearts**?

8. Why is it important to guard our **heart** in relationship to money and possessions?

9. What is the result of an unguarded **heart** related to money and possessions?

In the book, *Jesus Prom*, Jon Weece said of his dad, "My dad's name was Roy. He was the most generous man I have ever known. He taught me the value of one life. He taught me the value of one dollar—four quarters. Ten dimes—one hundred pennies."[60]

I would say that Jon's dad had a generous **heart**; what would you say? What a high compliment for a son to say of his dad that he was "the most generous man" he has ever known. What I desire is for the Father to say that of me as a daughter of His.

At this point in your life and walk with Christ, what would He say about your **heart** related to money and possessions? Would He be able to say unequivocally (without a doubt) that you possess a **generous** heart, a heart that **imitates** His heart? Ponder and pray over these questions.

10. In considering the questions above, write below what the Father revealed to you about the condition of your **heart**.

PONDER:

Money never stays with me. It would burn me if it did.
*I throw it out of my hands as soon as possible, lest it should find its way into my **heart**.[61]*
—John Wesley

MEDITATE:

*And I am praying that you will put into action the **generosity** that comes from your*
faith as you understand and experience all the good things we have in Christ.
Philemon 1:6 NLT

PRAY:

Lord, Your heart is a generous, obedient, and cheerful heart. Help me to emulate Your heart.
Help me to be generous as You are generous! All that I have is from You, so may I hold it
loosely lest You choose to bless others with the blessings You have bestowed upon me.
Amen!

[60]Jon Weece, *Jesus Prom*, (Nashville, Tennessee: Thomas Nelson, 2014). P. 109
[61] John Wesley, https://www.whatchristianswanttoknow.com/22-christian-quotes-about-money/#ixzz6lSMKGnWb

Day Three

Our neighborhood is a quaint little community tucked away from the rest of our suburban town. There are tree-lined streets and commons areas complete with benches and winding sidewalks. Many of the owners have a dog for a pet, some more than one. Because my desk faces the window in my office, quite often I see many of them as they walk their dogs. I can always tell those who have complete **mastery** over their pets. The dog stays by their side, never uses a neighbor's yard for doing his business, and does not jump on any one approaching him. That owner has complete **control** of his or her dog.

One of the definitions of **mastery** is *one having authority over another or one having control.* A dog with a master who has **control** over him is a **controlled** dog. He goes where the master wants him to go and does what the master wants him to do. In life, there are many things that have **mastery** over our lives. If you are in school, the headmaster or principal and the teachers have **mastery** over you. If you work a job outside the home, your boss has mastery over you. As Christians, God is supposed to have **mastery** over us. He is the one who we are to love and serve—not money or things!

If I love money more than Christ, woe is me! [62]
—William Tiptaft

1. List a few things in your life that would have **mastery** over your **heart** if not for self-control? Remember that mastery **means** authority or control over someone.

Often we can allow:

- Distractions to have **mastery** over us

- Discontentment to have **mastery** over us

- The voices of others to have **mastery** over us

- Busyness to have **mastery** over us

- Money to have **mastery** over us

 [62]William Tiptaft, https://www.christianquotes.info/quotes-by-author/william-tiptaft-quotes

2. In what ways can we allow money to have **mastery** over us?

> *How much better is it to let God be your Master?*[63] *—Neil S. Wilson*

Luke 16:13 says, "No one can serve two masters. Either you will hate the one and love the other, or you will be devoted to the one and despise the other. You cannot serve both God and money" (NIV).

3. Paul says you cannot serve God and money. Why is that? Explain.

4. Fill in the following blanks: "You must _____ the Lord your God and _____ _____ him" (Matthew 4:10b NLT).

> *Dear sister, be thankful for God's financial blessings, but also be alert to the effect money can have on your heart, on your spiritual life, and on the spiritual life of your family. Yes, you can master and manage your finances. But, beware—don't let it **master** you!*[64]
> *—Elizabeth George*

If money is the **master** of your heart and life—God is not! God says we are to serve Him and Him only.

If money is the **master** of your heart and life, others will know by the way you handle your money.

5. What does the way you spend your money say to others about what you love?

[63]Neil S. Wilson, *The Handbook of Bible Application* (Wheaton, Illinois: Tyndale House Publishers, Inc. 1992). P. 422-23
[64]Elizabeth George, *Life Management for Busy Women-Growth and Study Guide* (Eugene, Oregon: Harvest House Publishers, 2002). P. 85

- God wants the way we manage our money to be an expression of our love for Him.

- If we love Him we will allow Him **mastery** over all we have and others will know it!

Whoever says he abides in Him ought to walk in the same way in which He walked.
1 John 2:6 NRV

I love the way *The Message Bible* describes this verse from 1 John.

"If someone claims, 'I know him well!' but doesn't keep his commandments, he's obviously a liar. His life doesn't match his words. But the one who keeps God's word is the person in whom we see God's mature love. This is the only way to be sure we're in God. Anyone who claims to be intimate with God ought to live the same kind of life Jesus lived" (1 John 2:6).

6. Summarize the above verse in your own words related to the mastery of money.

Jesus allowed His Father to have **mastery** over everything He did while on earth—even His death!

If you have given Christ the rights, **mastery** over every dollar you have or ever will have, it will be reflected in the way you live.

7. How will allowing Christ the rights, **mastery** over every dollar you have or ever will have to be reflected in the way you live?

PONDER:

If a person gets his attitude toward money straight,
it will help straighten out almost every other area in his life.[65]
—Rev. Billy Graham

MEDITATE:

For the earth is the Lord's, and everything in it.
1 Corinthians 10:26 NLT

PRAY:

Lord, thank you for being Master of my heart, life, and all that I own.
May I continually relinquish authority and control to You, for You know best.
I want to walk on this earth as Jesus walked, loving and encouraging others,
living in a way that draws them to You, Father.
Amen!

[65]Rev. Billy Graham, Evangelist https://www.whatchristianswanttoknow.com/22-christian-quotes-about-money/#ixzz6lSLY3Am1

Day Four

Once when visiting family, my niece invited me to come and tour the home which she was house-sitting for a month. The home was quite lovely. It was evening when I arrived, the long lighted driveway made the entrance very captivating and elegant. The house sat on a large parcel of land and had three garages on each side of the beautiful glass encased front double doors. I entered by the side door and began the tour. I had never been in such a large, elegant home. There were three levels and a gorgeous back yard complete with pool and all the items for entertaining that a family would enjoy. I was taken back at the responsibility my niece had in **looking after** this lovely, massive home. The family had gone out of the country for a month and left her as the steward of their property.

To **steward** means *to manage or look after something belonging to someone else*. My niece was entrusted to **look after** this home, all ten thousand plus square feet of it! What an incredible responsibility!

1. In the *New Living Translation Bible*, there are several areas God admonishes us to **steward** well. According to the verses below what are a few of those?

1 PETER 4:10-11

EPHESIANS 5:15-16

1 TIMOTHY 6:18-19

God gives us **stewardship** or management over our spiritual gifts, time, and money—just to mention a few. Today, we are going to look at our **stewardship** over money.

Paul in speaking to the Corinthians says of those chosen by God to manage spiritual things, "Moreover, it is required of stewards that they be found trustworthy" (1 Corinthians 4:2 ESV).

2. Write the definition of the word **trustworthy**.

In **stewarding** the money God has given us, it is important to Him that we be trustworthy.

When teaching, Jesus often used parables, or what we would call "word pictures" to illustrate the lesson He was wanting His listeners to grasp.

3. Read the parable found in Matthew 25:14-30 (ESV). What is the lesson God was teaching us about the **stewardship** of money in this parable?

The bags of silver represent any resources we have been given, whether spiritual gifts, time, or money. God expects us to invest what He has given us wisely, no matter what it is. We are responsible to **look after** or **steward** well what He has given us.

In this parable, what was important was not the total amount earned but the faithfulness in utilizing what they were given. It is the same for us as **stewards** of what God has given us—how faithful will we be in utilizing it?

Remember that it is not how much we have but how well we use what we have.

Let's read about a man who stewarded well what he was given. This man was a faithful **steward** of Abraham's household and wealth.

Read Genesis 24.

[66]Donald S. Whitney, *Spiritual Disciplines for the Christian Life* (Colorado Springs, Colorado: NavPress, 1991). P. 141
[67]Chuck Swindoll, http://www.insight.org/resources/artivle-library/individual/god-owns-it-all

Through the years, Abraham found Eliezer to be faithful and dependable in **stewarding** his household and **managing** his wealth. So much so that he chose Eliezer for an important task.

4. Because Eliezer had proven himself to be a faithful **steward**, what task did Abraham assign him?

Abraham sent Eliezer hundreds of miles to find a wife that was spiritually suitable for Isaac. Eliezer had to find a woman who believed in the one true God. And, Eliezer succeeded in this task. With God's help, he found Rebekah, the future wife of Isaac, Abraham's son.

Eliezer was a faithful and good **steward**; therefore Abraham entrusted to him with the great and honorable responsibility of finding a wife for his son, Isaac. If we are faithful and good stewards of what God has entrusted to us, He will entrust us with more.

5. In what ways have you faithfully **stewarded** what God has given you?

6. If you were unable to answer the question above, what changes do you need to make in order to become a more faithful **steward** of what God has given you?

The Bible says, "When someone has been given much, much will be required in return; and when someone has been entrusted with much, even more will be required" (Luke 12:48b NLT).

If you have heard that line of wisdom before, you will know it means that we are held responsible for what we have been given. The talents, knowledge, time, and **wealth** we have been blessed with, we are to use effectively. The more He gives to us the greater the responsibility of our **stewardship**!

God will hold us responsible for our **stewardship** (management) of what we have been given!

PONDER:

No matter how much or little you have, as a believer you can
discipline yourself to use your money for the greatest purposes on earth:
for the glory of God and for the purpose of godliness.[68]
—Donald S. Whitney

MEDITATE:

The master was full of praise. 'Well done, my good and faithful servant.
You have been faithful in handling this small amount, so now I will give you many
more responsibilities. Let's celebrate together!
Matthew 25:21 NLT

PRAY:

God, be the Master of all that I am and all that I have. Father, help me to
be a good steward of all You have entrusted to me, seeking Your will,
Your wisdom, and Your direction. I want to be a trustworthy child.
Amen!

[68]Donald S. Whitney, *Spiritual Disciplines for the Christian Life* (Colorado Springs, Colorado: NavPress, 1991). P. 157

Day Five

A few years ago, God chose to place my husband, Mark, and me on a journey unlike any we had ever been on before. In stripping away all that I relied on—our income, our home, and Mark's health, God had my undivided attention. I was unaware at the time that one of His purposes was to change me from the inside out.

God exposed the condition of **my** heart related to money and **my** stuff. I was very dependent upon our income and **my** stuff. My attitude was one similar to many people today in that I felt I deserved what I had—and then some! It was in God's stripping away everything that He exposed the condition of my heart.

I was selfish in the area of **giving** because I wanted the monies for something that would bring me pleasure—more stuff! Giving anything beyond our tithe was a struggle for me because I saw those funds as **mine**. I want to share with you several things God revealed to me about the condition of **my** heart related to money and **my** stuff.

God revealed to me that I had an attitude of **entitlement**—I **deserved** this or that. But, I did not **deserve** anything. I came to realize that everything we owned was a gift from the Father. In His graciousness, He gave me what I did not **deserve**.

> *Whatever is good and perfect comes to us from God.*
> *James 1:17a NLV*

God revealed to me that **everything** I had was a result of **His blessings** in my life. He gave me a new perspective on **my** stuff by stripping away all that I relied upon. I began to see life differently, through spiritual eyes that for the first time could see all I had or ever would have as a great blessing in my life.

> *A faithful man will abound with blessings.*
> *Proverbs 28:20a ESV*

God revealed to me that I had **no right to hold on** to my money or my stuff. Because it is His, I have no right to it. He owns it all—I just manage (steward) it for Him.

O Lord, how many are Your works!
In wisdom You have made them all; the earth is full of Your possessions.
Psalm 104:24 NASB

God revealed to me that I was not living with an **open heart nor an open hand**. On this journey, God provided for us through the open hearts and hands of others. In seeing this, my heart was softened and humbled by those who understood the blessing and joy of open hands. I am now living with an open heart and open hands—it is so much fun—what a blessing and joy!

> *Give generously to the poor, not grudgingly, for the Lord your God will bless you in everything you do.*
> *Deuteronomy 15:10 NLT*

God revealed to me that any monies **He directed me** to give to others would not be missed. I want to give you an example of this principle:

I remember the day Mark called me into the family room of our rental home and said he had something to talk with me about. I sat down and he began telling me of all the starving widows in India and how they were placed at the bottom of the socioeconomic chain. He said many were below poverty level and were shunned in their culture. My heart went out to them, but I wondered what that had to do with us. At the rate we were going with no salary coming in due to his disabilities we were going to be at poverty level!

Then he said, "I think we need to support a widow in India; it's only $15 a month." "What?" I responded. "You want us to do what? Do you realize we have no income coming in?" (A sure sign of the condition of my heart at the time) Mark said that he had prayed about it, and this was what he felt God wanted us to do. Argue with that! One thing I knew for sure was that my husband walked closely with God and spent a great deal of time with Him. If he said that God said it, I was going to obey. So, we began that very week.

Six months later, Mark sat me down once more and said he felt the Lord wanted us to adopt a second widow. The look on my face made it clear how I felt. Certainly, one widow was enough! He asked if I had missed the fifteen dollars we'd been paying over those months. After a big gulp, I couldn't argue with the fact that God had provided, so I relinquished and wrote the check. At that point, we were giving our tithe and thirty dollars a month to two widows in India—all without an income.

> *A generous person will be blessed, for he shares his food with the poor.*
> *Proverbs 22:9 HCSB*

God revealed to me that **He knows all our needs and is fully capable of meeting each one according to His timing and His divine way**. I think God was quite entertained numerous times when I thought I had figured out just how He would meet several specific needs that we had. One was a desire for a home of our own, others were the funds to cover Mark's monthly life insurance payment, and the need for a reliable car.

- The monies for purchasing a lot to build the desired home to meet Mark's needs came through a friend, who raised the money from anonymous donors.

- The builders we met through a friend, and we were told after the closing on the house that they spent several thousand out of their own pockets to complete the house—now who does that for strangers?

- For over two years, we received an anonymous gift from a local bank for the exact amount of Mark's life insurance policy.

- The reliable car came as a result of a visit to Mark's siblings in Oklahoma. While we were there, they decided that we needed a reliable car and arranged to pay for it from Mark's inheritance prior to his mother's death.

> *My God will meet all your needs. He will meet them in keeping with his wonderful riches.*
> *These riches come to you because you belong to Christ Jesus.*
> *Philippians 4:19 NIRV*

Over these years, God has revealed to me that **He owns it all**. Because of this I have no ownership or right to what He has chosen to give me—it is all a blessing. I must hold it with an open hand. He owns it all; therefore, I can trust Him to meet my every need according to His timing and His divine way.

> *Whatever is under the whole heaven is mine. Job 41:11b ESV*

Read 2 Corinthians 9. Paul is admonishing the Corinthians to give to the church in Jerusalem.

1. According to these verses, what will God do for the one who is generous?

2. In verses 6-7 we see the Law of the Harvest. Explain this principle.

PONDER:

A man could have all the money in all the banks in all the world, and be worth nothing so far as God is concerned, if he were still living to and for himself.[69]
—Major Ian Thomas

MEDITATE:

The point is this: whoever sows sparingly will also reap sparingly, and whoever sows bountifully will also reap bountifully.
Each one must give as he has decided in his heart, not reluctantly or under compulsion, for God loves a cheerful giver.
2 Corinthians 9:6-7 ESV

PRAY:

Lord, nothing I have is deserved—it is all a gift from You. May all that You have given me be available for Your use and Your glory. My desire is to manage well what You have given me. Thank you for trusting me with Your riches.
Amen!

[69]Major Ian Thomas, https://www.whatchristianswanttoknow.com/22-christian-quotes-about-money/#ixzz6lSRMrWyK

Spinach and Bacon Quiche

One Pillsbury deep-dish ready to use pie crust

8 slices of bacon, cooked and chopped

¼ cup onion, chopped

4 large whole eggs, beaten

2 large egg whites, beaten

1 cup half and half

1 cup mild Swiss cheese, shredded

½ cup Cheddar cheese, shredded

¾ cup Parmesan cheese, shredded, divided

1 (10 ounce) chopped frozen spinach, thawed, drained

Preheat oven to 350°F. Bake unfilled pie shell according to package. In skillet, cook bacon, reserve drippings. Remove bacon, sauté onions in drippings then set aside. In large bowl, mix well whole eggs, egg whites, half and half, Swiss, Cheddar, and half of Parmesan cheese. Add drained spinach, onions, bacon, and stir well. Pour into pie shell, sprinkle remaining parmesan on top. Line baking sheet with foil to catch spills. Bake approximately 45 minutes, until center is firm. Let stand 10 minutes before serving. Optional: Serve with fresh fruit.

Dianne's Cheesy Garlic Grits

1 (32 ounce) carton of half and half

3 cups water

1 cup heavy cream

1 cup unsalted butter, cut in slices

½ tablespoon salt

1 teaspoon pepper

2 tablespoons garlic, minced

2½ cups grits, regular

2 eggs, beaten and tempered

16 to 24 ounces of shredded Cheddar cheese, divided

Preheat oven to at 350°F. Heat half and half, water, and heavy cream in large sauce pan on medium heat. When warmed thoroughly, add butter, stirring until melted. On medium-high bring to a slow boil; add salt and pepper, garlic and grits, stirring. Cover and reduce heat; simmer 10 to 15 minutes. Remove pan from burner and add tempered eggs and ¾ of the Cheddar cheese; stir until blended and cheese is melted. Pour into greased 9x13 baking dish. Top with remaining Cheddar cheese. Bake uncovered for 45 minutes, until bubbly. Note: Makes a large portion.

Lemon Blueberry Muffins

1 cup butter, softened

3 cups sugar

4 large eggs, room temperature

4 teaspoons vanilla

Juice of two lemons

Zest of two lemons

2 teaspoons lemon extract

2 cups sour cream

4½ to 5 cups all-purpose flour

1 teaspoon baking soda

2½ teaspoons baking powder

½ teaspoon salt

1½ cups fresh blueberries

Preheat oven to 375°F. In mixing bowl cream the butter and sugar until smooth and light in color. Blend in eggs one at a time. Add vanilla, lemon juice, zest, lemon extract, and sour cream. Mix thoroughly. Fold in flour, baking soda, baking powder, and salt into creamed mixture. Mix well. With a large spoon gently fold in blueberries. Line three 12-cup muffin tins with paper liners. Using a large ice cream scoop, place generous amounts of batter into paper-lined muffin tins. Batter should be firm and not topple. If it topples it may need a small amount of flour added. Bake for 25 to 30 minutes until lightly browned around the edges and muffins are set to the touch. Top with Lemon Glaze. Note: Makes 5 to 6 mini loaves, 2 large loaves or 36 to 48 muffins.

Lemon Glaze

4 tablespoons butter, melted

½ cup half and half

2 cups confectioners' sugar

¼ cup lemon juice

1 teaspoon pure lemon extract

In microwave, melt butter in glass mixing bowl. Add half and half and confectioners' sugar, blend well. Fold in lemon juice and lemon extract. Brush glaze over muffins while warm. Note: Whole milk may be substituted for half and half. This recipe makes an abundance of muffins. If you are only needing 24 muffins, cut the ingredients in half.

SHORT-CUTS...

- **SPINACH QUICHE:** Earlier in the day, cook bacon on cooling rack atop a jelly roll pan in oven at 400°F for 20 to 25 minutes. Cool and store. This method is less messy. In skillet, use drippings from jelly roll pan to brown onion.

- **DIANNE'S CHEESY GARLIC GRITS:** Earlier in the day, or a day ahead, prepare grits, cover, and refrigerate until ready to bake.

- **LEMON BLUEBERRY MUFFINS:** Day before, or earlier in the day, prepare and bake muffins. Cool. Store in zipper-lock bag. Reheat in 300°F oven wrapped in foil for 10 minutes or heat in the microwave.

HEALTHY TIPS...

- **SPINACH AND BACON QUICHE:** For a healthier dish, opt for a crust-less quiche. Grease pie pan and once ingredients are mixed thoroughly, pour into pan and bake according to directions.

- **SPINACH AND BACON QUICHE:** Substitute one cup chopped fresh spinach for frozen spinach.

- **SPINACH AND BACON QUICHE:** Use nitrate free bacon. In place of pre-shredded cheese, buy block and shred your own. This is better for you than the pre-shredded types.

- **DIANNE'S CHEESY GARLIC GRITS:** For a healthier dish, replace grits with cheesy cauliflower recipe.

- **LEMON BLUEBERRY MUFFINS:** Use unbleached flour and cut sugar by a 1 cup, using 2 cups.

- **LEMON BLUEBERRY MUFFINS:** If you desire to save calories and amount of sugar intake, top each muffin with ¼ teaspoon Turbinado (raw) sugar in place of glaze.

- **LEMON BLUEBERRY MUFFINS:** Choose a gluten-free muffin recipe if gluten-intolerant.

- **MENUS TOO HEAVY ON CARBS:** Serve fresh in-season fruit in place of grits or muffins.

Our Words

Remember that the tongue speaks only what is in the heart.

—Theodore Epp

Our Words Introduction

*T*o us, he was Dan, but to the horse world, he was better known by his competition name of Second Chance. He was a beautiful, chocolate brown, Quarter horse. One of the first times I was up close with Dan was when I was helping Kelly, our younger daughter, get his bit and bridle in place. You might say that Dan and I got off to a bad start. I do think he sensed my fear of horses. While I was standing beside his head, minding my own business, just waiting for instructions from Kelly, he bit me! Yes, he bit me!

I was totally innocent, yet with one fell swoop of his mouth, he came after me. With his mouth, he inflicted great pain. I not only wanted to get the bit and bridle on as quickly as possible, but I wanted to duct tape his mouth shut! Here we were providing room and board, a wool blanket, new shoes—nice expensive shoes at that—good feed and hay to eat, and he had the nerve to bite me! Needless to say, our relationship was a bit rocky from that day forward.

Over the years, I have been told to never stand behind a horse because it might kick you and never pull its tail or jerk too hard on the reigns; it might rear back. No one ever told me to beware of their mouths! Horses need to come with a warning sign: Beware! If you get too close—I will bite!

Come to think of it, many women could use that warning sign as well! Beware! If you get too close—she will bite! Often, we can inflict piercing hurt upon others with our mouths.

> *But no human being can tame the tongue. It is a restless evil, full of deadly poison. James 3:8 ESV*

James says that you and I cannot control our tongue. In and of ourselves, it is impossible. The Holy Spirit is to have control over our tongue, and when we refuse Him that control, we get into trouble. When I am about to say something I shouldn't, the Spirit whispers, "Dianne keep your mouth shut. What you are about to say is hurtful, unwise, and not honoring to you, the person you are speaking with, or Me." Do I always listen and obey? No. Why? Because my flesh wants its own way! When we ignore the Holy Spirit's voice and open our mouth, inflicting hurt and pain on others, we are in outright disobedience to the Father.

> *Therefore be imitators of God, as beloved children. And walk in love, as Christ loved us and gave himself up for us, a fragrant offering and sacrifice to God. Ephesians 5:1-2 NIV*

The words we use and the way we conduct our speech say a lot about our character. As believers, we are to imitate our heavenly Father in our attitudes, our actions, and our words.

The only one who can wreck your character is you[70] —*Leonard Ravenhill*

---

[70]Leonard Ravenhill, Article: *The Taming of the Tongue*, (Lindale, Texas, 1994). Ravenhill.org

Day One

Before cell phones, we had cassette tape players to record our words. I have an old one in my office that the grandchildren enjoy playing with when they are visiting. It is pretty simple to use. Just pop in the little cassette tape, if you can find one. Then push the play button and record button at the same time. As you speak it will record your words. If you do not like the way your message was worded, just push the back or reverse button until the tape returns to the beginning erasing your words and start over.

Oh, how many times have I wished that the words exiting my mouth could be reversed—erased from existence! But once they are out, there is no erasing them.

1. How can such a small part of the human anatomy wield such power? Explain how this happens.

Death and life are in the power of the tongue. Proverbs 18:21a ESV

---

2. Give an example of **words** that can bring about death and then those that bring about life.

WORDS THAT BRING ABOUT DEATH:

WORDS THAT BRING ABOUT LIFE:

Once again, just like with the subject of contentment and money, when it comes to our **words**, we must take a look at our **heart**. The root problem of discontentment and a desire for more, along with harmful words stems from the **heart**. Out of a wicked **heart** come deadly **words**, and out of a loving **heart** come words of life.

3. Fill in the blanks of the following verse. "But what comes out of the _____ comes from the _____, and this defiles a person" (Matthew 15:18 CSB).

4. Write the definition of the word **defile**.

In Chapter 15, Jesus is teaching about inner purity. The deep-seeded things in our **hearts** will come out through our mouths, and He says those things will defile us—will corrupt the purity of our **heart**.

> *We work hard to keep the outward appearance attractive, but what is deep down in our heart (where others cannot see) is more important to God. What are you like inside? When people become Christians, God makes them different on the inside. He will continue the process of change inside them if they only ask. God wants us to have healthy thoughts and motives, not just healthy bodies.*[71] *NLT Parallel Study Bible*

In the above quote, the question was asked, "What are you like inside?" Only you and God can answer that question. Through introspection, you can answer that question. God knows you. If you ask Him what He sees—He will tell you.

Examine your heart. From what Jesus said in Matthew 15, our hearts control our tongue!

5. Out of your **heart** come thoughts that are expressed through **words**. Is your **heart** one of love or is it a wicked, defiled, corrupt, and impure **heart**? Pray and ask God to help you see what He sees when He looks at your **heart**. Below write a prayer related to what God revealed to you about the condition of your **heart**.

[71]*NLT Parallel Study Bible* (Carol Stream, Illinois: Tyndale House Publishing, 2011). P. 1779

When we want to ignore something someone has said on Facebook or by text we push delete. Poof! The **words** are gone! But the **words** we verbalize cannot be deleted. Once our **words** are out, we cannot get them back. They have been seen or heard by those reading or listening—and seen and heard by God.

Leonard Ravenhill said of his mother, "My mother was pretty smart when it came to the tongue. She sprinkled her daily conversation with wise sayings like 'Keep your tongue between your teeth' and 'Think twice before you speak once.' My mother would also tell us, 'Remember, one day you'll answer to God for every word you say.'"[72]

PONDER:

*The showcase of the **heart** is the **tongue**.*[73]
—Leonard Ravenhill

MEDITATE:

I tell you, on the day of judgment you will have to give an account for every careless word you utter ...
Matthew 12:36 NRSV

PRAY:

Father, Oh that my words would be words of life and not words of
death and destruction. Examine my heart and let me see what You see.
If there is defilement or corruption in my heart, make it clean once again.
Do Your divine work from the inside out making my life,
my thoughts, and my words a reflection of You.
Amen!

[72]Leonard Ravenhill, Article: *The Taming of the Tongue*, (Lindale, Texas, 1994). Ravenhill.org
[73]Leonard Ravenhill, Article: *The Taming of the Tongue*, (Lindale, Texas, 1994). Ravenhill.org

Day Two

It turned out to be a beautiful Sunday afternoon for a wedding shower, almost 60 degrees with the sun shining that day, which was a blessing. As a hostess, when you plan a winter shower you never know about the weather.

In certain settings, such as a shower, we as women can find ourselves feeling like an outsider, especially if our circumstances are quite different from others attending the event. Since my husband, Mark, passed away, I can feel like an outsider and very alone in certain settings. Because of this, the day before the shower, I began praying about my time there. I found myself praying that instead of focusing on myself that God would reveal to me those who needed a word of **encouragement**.

1. Write Colossians 4:6 NIV below.

In her book, *A Woman After God's Own Heart*, Elizabeth George says of the above verse, "You have the ministry of salting—the ministry of **encouragement**—with everyone you meet. If you 'let your speech always be with grace, seasoned with salt' (Colossians 4:6), you will never fail to minister to those you encounter. Your life and lips will offer refreshing **encouragement** to all who cross your path."[74]

When we are feeling insecure, threatened, left out, or emotionally low, our words can often reflect those feelings. What comes out of our mouths in those times is a direct result of what is in our **heart**. Often, those **words** do not honor the person, ourselves, or God. When we respond out of envy, insecurity, loneliness, or an emotional low, our words can be as poison to others rather than a soothing balm.

2. Do you find that your *feelings*, those things in the deep recesses of your **heart**, often impact your **words**? Explain.

3. Remember Matthew 15:18 (CSB) from yesterday's study? What is in our **hearts** will make its way out through our mouths! So, according to Proverbs 4:23, what must we do with our **hearts**?

[74]Elizabeth George, *A Women After God's Own Heart*, (Eugene, Oregon: Harvest House Publishers, 1997.) P. 207

Every **word** we speak is a reflection of the person we are, the heart we possess, and the relationship we have with our Creator. We must consider our words carefully!

4. Fill in the following blanks: "For by your _____ you will be justified, and by your _____ you will be condemned" (Matthew 12:37 ESV).

5. Write the definition of the word **justified**.

6. Write the definition of the word **condemned**.

Using the definitions above, let's rewrite Matthew 12:37, "For by your **words** you *are declared or made righteous in the sight of God*, and by your **words** you are declared *unfit for use*" (ESV).

7. Does placing the definitions within this verse change the way in which you interrupt it? Explain.

Do you want your **words** declared or made righteous in the sight of God or declared unfit for use? Only you can determine which!

Justified **words** are **words** that bless others while condemned **words** would be **words** that are unfit for use, **words** that bring curses instead of blessings in the lives of others—and in your life!

8. In the book of Acts, we are introduced to a disciple named Joseph. According to Acts 4:36, what was Joseph's nickname?

Joseph, nicknamed Barnabas, meaning "son of encouragement," **encouraged** Paul and was an **encouragement** to him in his ministry.

9. Place your name in the following blank: How would it make you feel if people referred to you as:_____, woman of **encouragement**? What if all your **words** were **words** of **encouragement** instead of **words** unfit for use or curses?

Stop right now and pray asking God to guard your **heart** because out of it flows **words** that can either bless or curse, declare you righteous and fit before God, or declare you and your **words** unfit before God.

As I was driving home from the shower, I was recounting all the sweet conversations I experienced. I was not wrestling with feelings of being left out or insecure, rather just a feeling of gratitude that God had used me to bless and **encourage** others. I left with a spirit of joy and peace, and not a spirit of regret!

PONDER:

I guard my ways that I might not sin with my tongue; I will guard my mouth as with a muzzle (Psalm 39:1). We usually think of other parts of our body as agencies of sin, but not our tongue. David says, 'I will guard my mouth.'[75]
—Leonard Ravenhill

MEDITATE:

Whoever watches his mouth and tongue keeps himself from trouble.
Proverbs 21:23 ISV

PRAY:

Father, my heart is the main channel for my attitudes and words.
Cleanse it of any unclean and unfit emotion that dwells there. Help my words
to be righteous and fit before You, blessing those around me. May the words
of my mouth and the meditations of my heart honor You and others.
Amen!

---

[75]Leonard Ravenhill, Article: *The Taming of the Tongue*, (Lindale, Texas, 1994). Ravenhill.org

Day Three

I read of a professor at Princeton University who ran an experiment to test the rapidity of gossip. He called six students to his office and in strict confidence shared with them that the Duke and Duchess of Windsor were planning on attending an event on the university campus. Within a week this totally fictitious story had reached over 2,000 students. The City officials were demanding of the school more information and asking why they were not told of the Duke and Duchess' arrival. Numerous press agencies were in a panic and wanting details of their visit. From this experiment, the professor observed, "That was a pleasant rumor—a slanderous one travels even faster."[76]

Unfortunately, he is right! His observation is correct. Destructive and slanderous words, gossip, and rumors travel faster than a speeding bullet.

God has much to say about gossip and slander.

Read the verse: "Do not go around saying things that **hurt** your people" (Leviticus 19:16a NLV).

1. Write the above verse from Leviticus in the New Living Translation below.

2. Write the definition of the word **slander**.

3. Write the definition of the word **gossip**.

We must take seriously God's clear warning in Leviticus, "Do not spread **slanderous gossip** among your people" (NLT). This warning was given from God, through Moses, to the people. In this same chapter, God gave personal conduct guidelines for living a righteous life.

[76]https://bible.org/seriespage/lesson-13-have-you-heard-about-gossip-2-samuel-13-15

Along with this guideline or warning in this passage are other important warnings: respect your parents, trust God not your things, do not steal, do not cheat, do not swear falsely, do not seek revenge, and obey God's decrees. Following several of the guidelines God refers to Himself, "I am the Lord your God," "I am the Lord," and "I am holy." In saying this, He was reminding the Israelites, and us, that we are to obey God's Word. We are to be holy as He is holy. God is serious about His Word. When he says, "Do not spread **slanderous gossip**," we are not to spread **slanderous gossip**.

> *A rolling stone gathers no moss, but a rolling story gathers something fresh every time we say it. Every time we repeat it, something is added and something is taken away until it's nothing like the truth. Some little bit of **gossip** starts with a whisper, then it swells and becomes a tumult, and somebody's left heartbroken."*
> —*Leonard Ravenhill*

4. Do you find this statement of Leonard Ravenhill's true? **No**_____ **Yes**_____ Explain.

Gossip and **slander** are hurtful to others. If you have ever been the recipient of someone's gossip or slander, you know this to be true.

As a tree gives us fruit, healing words give us life. But evil words crush the spirit. Proverbs 15:4 ICB

God takes very seriously the ways in which we communicate (use our words) with others. We can see from scripture that **gossiping** about others angers our heavenly Father, just as an earthly father becomes angry with his children for hurting one another.

5. Fill in the blanks of the following verse: "If you claim to be _____ but don't _____your _____, you are _____ yourself, and your _____ is _____" (James 1:26 NLT).

These are strong words! But according to this verse, the religion of those who **slander** is worthless. We cannot **slander** and **gossip** about others and call ourselves Christ-like. What comes out of our mouths is a clear indication of our character—what is in our **hearts**! Remember the words of Matthew 12:34b.

[77]Leonard Ravenhill, Article: *The Taming of the Tongue*, (Lindale, Texas, 1994). Ravenhill.org

> *For whatever is in your **heart** determines what you say.* NLT

Are you seeing a pattern from these weeks of study? The **heart** is the root of what is good or evil in our lives and what honors or dishonors God and others. The **heart** is the **base of operation** for our actions and attitudes as a Christian. If you **gossip**—check your **heart**!

Is **slanderous gossip** a sin? From what we have seen today in scripture, there is no doubt that the answer to that question is **yes**. The Bible says that all sin carries the death penalty (Romans 6:23). Sin separates us from God. Just as a bridge separates one body of land from another, sin separates us from God.

6. How can you know when words spoken about someone crosses the line into sinful **gossip**?

While we might be tempted to rank **gossip** as just a tiny, inconsequential sin, we must remember that all sin is spiritually fatal unless we repent of it!

> *We tolerate **gossip** because we've all been guilty of it. It's easy to condemn people for sins you've never committed, but it's not so easy to face up to sin which you have done and have encouraged others to do by listening to their **gossip**. So we tend to shrug it off. Or we spiritualize it: 'I just wanted you to know so that you could pray.' But we need to own up to **gossip** as a serious sin that can destroy people.*[78] —*Steven J. Cole*

Pray and ask God to show you if you are guilty of **gossiping** about others. Confess what He reveals, and ask Him to forgive you—He will!

[78]Steven J. Cole, Article: *Have You Heard About Gossip* (www.bible.org, 1993).

PONDER:

Five questions to ask when being drawn into gossip:

- **What is the reason you are telling me this?** *You're asking the person their motive for sharing this information with you.*

- **Where did you receive your information?** *If a person refuses to identify the source of information, she is probably spreading an evil report.*

- **Have you gone to those directly involved?** *If a person has not done this, she is not interested in helping restore an offender, but only in spreading gossip.*

- **Have you personally checked out all of the facts?** *Often, gossip is based on hearsay or misinformation. Or the person spreading it has listened to only one side.*

- **Can I quote you if I decide to check this out?** *A gossip doesn't want to be quoted because she's not sure of her facts and she doesn't want to be involved in the solution.*

MEDITATE:

Who may worship in your sanctuary, Lord? Who may enter your presence on your holy hill? Those who lead blameless lives and do what is right, speaking the truth from sincere hearts. Those who refuse to gossip or harm their neighbors or speak evil of their friends.
Psalm 15:1-3 NLT

PRAY:

Lord, may the words that flow from my mouth bring life and not death to those who hear them. I don't want to be known as a gossiping woman, one who wounds others with her words. Daily I desire to place my flesh under the submission of Your Spirit. I want to have a pure heart. Use me as a vessel of love and encouragement to others!
Amen.

Day Four

I have discovered that the longer I am involved in a cell conversation, the greater the chances are that my **words** will turn in a direction that is not always honoring to others. Years ago, I read where author, Elizabeth George, said she keeps her cell conversations to fifteen minutes. She said every woman should be able to say what needs to be said in that amount of time—or less.

> *When there are many **words**, sin is **unavoidable**, but the one who **controls** his lips is **wise**.*
> *Proverbs 10:19 HCSB*

1. What is it about long conversations that makes it a possibility that things will be said that should not have been said?

Research shows that women speak about 20,000 words a day, approximately 13,000 more than the average man.[79]

Just because we have all those **words** does not mean we need to use them! Self-control is a discipline, an exercise.

2. Write the definition of the word **self-control**.

3. List several synonyms for **self-control**.

[79]www.dailymail.co.uk/.../women-really-talk-men-13,000-words-day-percise.hmtl

4. Write the definition of the word **discipline**.

According to the definitions, we as Christian women need to **practice training** our tongues to behave in a **controlled way**—a way that honors God, us, and others.

5. Write Galatians 5:22-23 below.

In verse 16 of this chapter, Paul says, "So I say, let the Holy Spirit guide your lives." He goes on to speak of the sinful nature versus the Spirit filled life. He says, "And the Spirit gives us desires that are the opposite of what the sinful nature desires." He lists the sins that are the result of following the sinful nature. He then says that the Holy Spirit living within a believer will produce fruit—**self-control** being one.

Jerry Bridges says in, *The Discipline of Grace*, "The Bible was not given just to increase our knowledge but to guide our conduct."[80]

Paul's words are here to **guide our conduct**—the conduct of our mouths! Our words are to be under the Holy Spirit's control not the flesh's control!

> *Conquering one's self is what the Spirit's fruit of **self-control** is all about.*
> ***Self-control** is the controlling power of the will under the operation of the Spirit of God,*
> *literally a holding in of one's self with a firm hand by means of the Spirit.*
> *In simple terms; self-control is the ability to keep one's self in check.[81]*
> *—Elizabeth George*

The Spirit's fruit of self-control is not only keeping self in check, but our words in check!

[80]Jerry Bridges, *The Discipline of Grace* (Colorado Springs, Colorado: Nav Press, 2006). P. 187
[81]Elizabeth George, *A Woman's Walk with God*, (Eugene, Oregon: Harvest House Publishers, 1997.) P. 186

When we submit to the control of the Spirit, the fruit of **self-control** is evident in our lives. According to Elizabeth George in her book, *A Woman's Walk with God*, there are five things that having **self-control** does for us:

- **Self-control** controls and checks self (The motivation of our words)

- **Self-control** restrains self (The amount of our words)

- **Self-control** disciplines and masters self (The control of our words)

- **Self-control** holds in and commands self (The restraint of our words)

- **Self-control** says, "No!" to self (The "No" to self-centered words)[82]

When we practice training our tongues to behave in a controlled way by exercising self-control, we will honor God, ourselves, and others.

Once we have mastered the **discipline** and **control** of our **words**, we must learn to exercise the **discipline of listening**—which is much harder for us as women. Controlling or withholding a few of our 20,000 words can be a challenge!

6. Read James 1:19. What does James tell us we should be quick to do? Slow to do?

   QUICK TO _____. **SLOW TO** _____.

> *My dear brothers and sisters, take note of this: Everyone should be quick to listen, slow to speak and slow to become angry.*
> *James 1:19 NIV*

7. Write Proverbs 15:28 ESV below.

[82]Elizabeth George, *A Woman's Walk with God*, (Eugene, Oregon: Harvest House Publishers, 1997.) P. 190

PONDER:

Man has harnessed the wind with giant windmills, and made the rivers and waterfalls drive our turbines. What incredible power man has over the world! And yet, he has still not conquered his own tongue.[83]
—*Leonard Ravenhill*

MEDITATE:

The one who guards his words guards his life; but whoever is talkative will come to ruin.
Proverbs 13:3 NET

PRAY:

Oh Lord, may You have mastery over my words. Help me to be slow to speak and quick to listen. May I listen intently that I might be an encouragement to others. May my words be few and my love abundant! As a Christian woman, make me an ever-flowing current of Your grace and love toward others.
Amen!

[83]Leonard Ravenhill, Article: *The Taming of the Tongue*, (Lindale, Texas, 1994). Ravenhill.org

Day Five

I was trying to concentrate on my workout but found myself **distracted** by a loud male voice. Looking around the gym, I saw a young man on an elliptical wearing earbuds and carrying on a conversation as if he were seated in his den. It became very annoying. I wanted to tell him that just because he was in a public place did not mean that his conversation needed to be public. Everyone working out that day was a part of his conversation whether we wanted to be or not!

Have you ever been in a stall of a women's public restroom while the woman in the stall next to you was having a private conversation on her cell phone? You don't want to eavesdrop but what choice do you have? When in a public place, all cell phone conversations become public and are a **distraction** to those overhearing them. Who wants to hear the ongoing plethora of words from the mouths of others? Our **words** are not always to be "public" **words**.

The amount of **words** we take in everyday can be a **distraction** in our lives. "Research suggests that the average person hears between 20,000 and 30,000 **words** during the course of a twenty-four hour period."[84]

If the average person hears 20,000 to 30,000 **words** in a twenty-four hour period, can you imagine how many God hears?

God hears every **word** we speak, every song we sing in worship, every whisper uttered in our prayers, and even every **word** spoken in the heart. While there are billions of people talking, shouting, singing, or whispering on our planet, He can recognize every **word** we say. It is an incredible thought but also an incredible responsibility as to how we use our words. What is even more incredible is that God knows all our **words** before we express them.

1. Fill in the blanks of the following verse: "You _____ what I am going to _____ even _____ I _____ it, Lord" (Psalm 139:4 NLT).

2. How does knowing that God hears your every **word** and that He knows your every **word** (before you express it) change the way you look at the use of your **words**?

So, if God knows our **words** and hears our **words**, let's see what we learn from James as to right Christian behavior related to the tongue.

The book of James was written by Jesus' brother, James. One of the purposes of his writings was to teach **right** Christian behavior. He refers to the **tongue** and our **words** in many verses within the book. Obviously, God knew the issue of the **tongue** needed to be addressed knowing it could be an instrument of ungodly behavior—if not **guarded**.

Read James 3:1-12.

[84]Rebecca Lake, Article: *Listening Statistics: 23 Facts You Need to Hear* (creditdonkey.com, September 17, 2010.)

3. In chapter 3:1-2, James addresses those Christians who aspire to become teachers (leaders). The **responsibility** is greater for those who lead or teach. What was he saying about their **words** and actions?

James is saying that our **responsibility** as Christians is great because our **words** and example affect the spiritual lives of others.

> *The more opportunity you have to give out the Word of God, the greater is your responsibility to God Himself.*[85]
> —*J. Vernon McGee*

4. In chapter 3:3-4, James uses two word pictures for controlling the **tongue**. Explain each and its application.

5. Write what David said about his **tongue** in Psalm 39:1 below.

6. What had David resolved to do?

7. In chapter 3:5b-6, James likens the damage a **tongue** can do to what? Explain the implication of these verses.

[85]J. Vernon McGee, *Thru the Bible with J. Vernon McGee* (Nashville, Tennessee: Thomas Nelson Publishers, 1983). P. 654

8. What is James' ultimate conclusion about the tongue in verses 7-12?

Years ago, some young men from our church came and rolled (choose your terminology based on your part of the country) our home. Sure enough, we woke the next morning to our trees being covered in Charmin. We lived on the corner of a major road so my husband was anxious to get the paper cleaned up. A friend of ours said that he had gotten rid of the toilet paper in their yard by lighting each strip and letting it burn until it fell from the tree. So, we decided to try it. Mark got the lighter and set the first strip on fire. The fire ran up that toilet paper as if it had been doused in gasoline. The only problem was that it was winter and everything was dry, so the fire not only burned the toilet paper strip but began to spread across the branch of the tree. It was amazing how quickly the fire spread and the damage it did in a short amount of time.

Our **words** can be like that fire, spreading quickly and doing a great deal of damage! Knowing that God hears each **word** should cause us to **stop** and **think** before we speak.

A heart of devotion to God will exhibit a controlled **tongue** from which flows **words** that bless and encourage others. But out of a wicked distracted heart will flow **words** that burn and bring damage to others. God **hears** your every **word**, and He knows your every **word**—so guard your **tongue** and **your fingers**—for they can either bless or hurt others through texting, emailing, or gossiping.

PONDER:

*The tongue reveals genuine faith, because it is with the mouth
that confession is made of that which is in the heart.*[86]
—*J. Vernon McGee*

MEDITATE:

*The tongues of those who do right are like fine silver. But the hearts of those who do
wrong aren't worth very much. The words of those who do right benefit many people.
But those who are foolish die because they have no sense.*
Proverbs 13:3 NET

PRAY:

*Lord, my heart is broken to think of the many times my words have spread like
a wild fire inflicting damage upon others. Forgive me for not controlling my tongue.
Help me to express words that are pleasing to You and encouraging to others.
Guard my tongue, but also my fingers, for they can inflict damage through texting, emailing
and gossiping. Cleanse my heart so that out of it will flow words of blessings.*
Amen!

 [86]J. Vernon McGee, *Thru the Bible with J. Vernon McGee* (Nashville, Tennessee: Thomas Nelson Publishers, 1983). P. 657

Week Six Menu

Roast Beef Sliders

3 to 4 pounds rump roast/top round roast

1 cup water

1 cup salsa (Mateo's recommended)

1 (1 ounce) packet Au Jus mix

1 (1 ounce) packet Italian dressing mix

1 (2 ounce) packet onion soup mix

Place roast in a slow cooker. Whisk together water and three seasoning packets. Pour mixture and salsa over roast. Cook on high for first hour; reduce, cook on low for additional 7 hours.

FOR SLIDERS:

1 package King's Hawaiian rolls

½ cup butter, melted

1 package cheese slices, your choice

Cut each roll in half and place on cookie sheet. Butter and place cheese slice on top half. Broil 1 to 2 minutes until lightly browned and cheese bubbles. Remove from oven. Shred roast and place spoonful onto each roll. Drizzle with Creamy Chipotle Sauce and serve.

CREAMY CHIPOTLE SAUCE:

¼ cup sour cream

2 teaspoons horseradish

2 tablespoons chili sauce

Mix ingredients well and chill.

Sweet Potato Fries with a Kick

2 tablespoons butter

2 medium sweet potatoes, peeled,
cut into ½ inch strips

¼ cup Parmesan cheese, grated

½ teaspoon salt

1 teaspoon chili powder

⅛ teaspoon ground red pepper

Preheat oven to 425°F. Place melted butter in large bowl; add sweet potatoes. Toss to coat. Add all remaining ingredients; toss to thoroughly coat sweet potatoes. Arrange sweet potatoes in a single layer on baking sheet. Bake for 40 to 45 minutes, turning once, until golden brown.

Jumbo Chocolate Chip Cookies

½ cup butter, softened

½ cup shortening

1 cup brown sugar, firmly packed

½ cup sugar

2 large eggs

2 teaspoons vanilla

2½ cups all-purpose flour

1 teaspoon baking soda

½ teaspoon salt

2 cups semi-sweet chocolate morsels

1 cup pecans, chopped (Optional)

Preheat oven to 375°F. Beat butter and shortening at medium speed with mixer until creamy. Gradually add sugars, beating well. Add eggs one at a time and vanilla, beat well. Combine flour, baking soda, and salt, gradually add to butter mixture, just until combined. Stir in chocolate chips and pecans. Drop dough with medium cookie scoop onto un-greased baking sheet. Bake for 9 minutes. Cool slightly on baking sheets; remove to wire racks to cool completely.

Milky Way Ice Cream

8 Milky Way bars, sliced

2 cups whole milk

5 eggs, room temperature

1½ cups sugar

2 teaspoons vanilla

1 (13 ounce) can evaporated milk

2½ cups half and half

In heavy saucepan over medium-heat, melt candy bars in 2 cups of milk, stirring continually. Cool. Beat eggs, add sugar and mix well. Add vanilla, evaporated milk, and half and half. Combine the chocolate with the egg mixture, mixing well. Pour mixture into freezer canister. Add extra milk if needed to fill to full line. Freeze in the ice cream freezer. Once set, stir well and freeze in a refrigerator freezer for 2 to 3 hours before serving.

SHORT-CUTS...

- **ROAST BEEF SLIDERS:** To prepare sliders ahead, place roast in slow cooker and let cook during the night while you sleep. Cool. Shred and store until ready to prepare sandwiches.

- **SWEET POTATO FRIES WITH A KICK:** Morning off, peel and cut sweet potato fries. Place in bowl of water and refrigerate all day. Remove, drain, and return to room temperature. Pat dry before coating with oil.

- **JUMBO CHOCOLATE CHIP COOKIE:** Cookies can be made days ahead and frozen.

- **ICE CREAM** can be made up to 3 to 4 days ahead and stored in an air-tight container in freezer.

HEALTHY TIPS...

- **FOR SLIDERS:** Use grass-fed beef. The roast beef requires eight hours to cook in a *Crock-Pot*, so put it on to cook early the morning or cook the night before serving the next day.

- **HOMEMADE DRESSING:** To avoid preservatives and additives make your own homemade Dry Italian Dressing Mix and Dry Onion Soup Mix.

- **HOMEMADE SAUCE:** Make homemade Au Jus sauce, using Organic broth and unbleached flour.

- **WHOLE WHEAT:** Serve on 100% whole wheat buns or eliminate the bread and serve beef topped with Chipotle Sauce.

- **SWEET POTATO FRIES WITH A KICK:** 7 Reasons to consider sweet potatoes over white potatoes:

  1. They are high in vitamin B6 and are a good source of vitamin C as well as potassium.

  2. They contain Vitamin D which is critical for immune system and overall health. D plays an important role in our energy levels, moods, and helps to build healthy bones, heart, nerves, skin, and teeth, and it supports the thyroid gland.

  3. Sweet potatoes contain iron and are a good source of magnesium. Magnesium is necessary for healthy artery, blood, bone, heart, muscle, and nerve function.

  4. Sweet potatoes are naturally sweet-tasting, but their natural sugars are slowly released into the bloodstream, helping to ensure a balanced and regular source of energy.

  5. Their rich orange color indicates that they are high in carotenoids like beta carotene and other carotenoids, which is the precursor to vitamin A in your body. Carotenoids help strengthen our eyesight and boost our immunity to disease; they are powerful antioxidants that help ward off cancer and protect against the effects of aging.

  6. They are versatile. Try them roasted, puréed, steamed, baked, or grilled.

- **JUMBO CHOCOLATE CHIP COOKIE:** Use unbleached all-purpose flour, coconut sugar, and carob chips. This is the best we can do!

Self-Control

But I cannot, by direct moral effort,
give myself new motives. After the first few
steps in the Christian life we realize that
everything which really needs to be done in
our souls can be done only by God.

—C.S. Lewis

While talking with a friend about self-control, I told her that I was proud of myself for exercising self-control at the grocery store that day. As usual, I was making my way through the store from the produce section on one side to the dairy section on the other side. My normal pattern is to go along the back of the store, bypassing most of the aisles containing items I do not need. That particular day, when I finished in the dairy section, I cut across the middle of the store, ending in the ice cream section. As I approached, I heard my favorite ice cream calling my name. "Dianne, here right here. See here I am, the Chocolate Peanut Butter flavor—your favorite. Come, partake and enjoy. Drown all your worries and your woes in me." In spite of the temptation, I resisted! I walked right by and glanced back as if to say, "No! You will not tempt me this time! My will is stronger than my fleshly desire for Chocolate Peanut Butter ice cream!"

My friend said that she had a similar experience that day at the store, not with ice cream, but with the jelly beans. Easter just happened to be a few weeks away, and the store display was loaded with jelly beans. She said, unlike me, her flesh won out, and her self-control evaporated as she passed the Easter display. She heard the jelly beans calling her name, bought them, and ate the entire bag that afternoon. We got tickled thinking that the sum total of this lesson on **self-control** revolves around avoiding the ice cream and Easter candy section of the grocery store!

Though that summation seems humorous—there is some truth to it, especially when you consider the dictionary definition of **self-control**. It is defined as *the ability to control oneself, in particular one's emotions and desires or the expression of them in one's behavior, especially in difficult situations*. The only way to control ourselves, apart from the indwelling of the Holy Spirit, is for us to avoid circumstances and difficult situations that will test our **self-control**.

Watchman Nee, persecuted Chinese writer and preacher said, "If we know that the aim of the Holy Spirit is to lead man to the place of **self-control**, we shall not fall into passivity but shall make good progress in spiritual life. The fruit of the Spirit is **self-control**."[87]

In Galatians 5:19-23, Paul describes to us the result of submission to our fleshly desires versus the result of submission to the indwelling of the Holy Spirit. He says, "When you follow the desires of your sinful nature, the results are very clear: sexual immorality, impurity, lustful pleasures, idolatry, sorcery, hostility, quarreling, jealousy, outbursts of anger, selfish ambition, dissension, division, envy, drunkenness, wild parties, and other sins like these. Let me tell you again, as I have before, that anyone living that sort of life will not inherit the Kingdom of God. But the Holy Spirit produces this kind of fruit in our lives: love, joy, peace, patience, kindness, goodness, faithfulness, gentleness, and self-control. There is no law against these things!" (NLT).

Watchman Nee understood that he had to allow the Holy Spirit full control of his emotions and desires if he was to live a life of **self-control**—and so must we!

for God gave us a spirit not of fear but of power and love and self-control.
2 Timothy 1:7 ESV

Day One

Most of us would claim that we have good **self-control**, unless that is, we are pushed, prodded, pressured, tempted, or lose the ability to direct the course of our own lives. I think the greatest test of our **self-control** is how we respond when our lives are out of **our** control. Due to the disease that was overtaking his body, my husband, Mark, could no longer direct the course of his own life. After battling Multiple Systems Atrophy for seven years, he came to the place of not being able to dress, bathe, shave, go to the bathroom, or feed himself. Everything in his life was controlled by someone else. In the midst of that, I observed something amazing—he never got frustrated, impatient, or irritated with the ways in which others cared for him. He had no control of his life, yet he remained **self-controlled**! He was sweet, kind, and appreciative.

Many of us are just the opposite: sweet, kind, appreciative, and **self-controlled** as long as things are going **our** way—as long as we can direct **our** own life.

The Biblical definition of **self-control** is *restraint exercised over one's own impulses, emotions, or desires*. Mark definitely displayed restraint. It was evident to those who spent any time with him that he had relinquished his impulses, emotions, and desires to the Father—the Holy Spirit was the **controlling** factor in his life.

> *We must have a spirit of power towards the enemy, a spirit of love*
> *towards men, and a spirit of **self-control** towards ourselves.*[88]
> *—Watchman Nee*

1. Read 2 Peter 1:3-7 NLT, then fill in the following blanks: "By his divine power, God has given us _____ we need for living a _____ life. We have received all of this by coming to _____ him, the one who called us to himself by means of his marvelous _____ and excellence. And because of his glory and excellence, he has _____ us great and precious promises. These are the promises that _____ you to share his divine _____ and escape the world's corruption caused by _____ desires. In view of all this, make every _____ to respond to God's promises. Supplement your _____ with a generous provision of _____ excellence, and _____ excellence with knowledge, and knowledge with _____, and _____ with patient endurance, and patient endurance with godliness, and godliness with brotherly affection, and brotherly affection with _____ for everyone."

Peter is saying that the power to live a godly life comes from God. You and I don't have the resources to be truly godly, but because He allows us to share in His divine nature, we have power over sin. "When we are born again, God by His Spirit empowers us with His goodness"[89] (NLT Parallel Study Bible).

[88] Watchman Nee, www.christianquotes.com/selfcontrol/wtachmannee
[89] *NLT Parallel Study Bible* (Carol Stream, Illinois: Tyndale House Publishing, 2011). P. 2378

2. Faith is much more than belief in facts; it must result in action and the growth of Christian character. It requires the practice of moral disciplines. Peter gives several moral disciplines or faith actions in verses 3-5. List them below.

3. When you are pushed, prodded, pressured, tempted, or lose the ability to direct the course of your own life, how do you respond?

4. Using a scale of 1-10, with 10 being totally **self-controlled**, where would you rank yourself on an average day?

5. If your score was below 10, what are the things that cause you to lose your **self-control**?

Paul asked the question in 1 Corinthians 3:16, "Do you not know that you are God's temple and that God's Spirit lives in you?"

As a born-again believer, you have the Holy Spirit living in you—but does He control you? That is the question! If you are allowing the Holy Spirit complete control in your life—it will show. You will be able to maintain **self-control** when life is out of control!

We are saved so that we can grow to resemble Christ and serve others.
God wants to produce His character in us. But, to do this He demands our discipline
*and effort. As we obey Christ, who guides us by His Spirit, we will develop **self-control**,*
not only with respect to food and drink, but also with respect to our emotions.[90]
NLT Parallel Study Bible

---

[90]*NLT Parallel Study Bible* (Carol Stream, Illinois: Tyndale House Publishing, 2011). P. 2378

When I think of an example in the Bible of one whose life was out of control, yet retained her **self-control**, I think of Esther. She was a woman who remained **self-controlled** in the midst of a challenging life situation.

Read the short book of Esther and see how she remains **self-controlled** in the most difficult of circumstances.

6.   In what ways and under what circumstances did Esther exhibit **self-control**?

It was Esther's faith in God that allowed her to respond to King Xerxes, the ill treatment of Haman, and the requests of her relative, Mordecai with **self-control**. We have nothing within us that is strong enough or powerful enough to stand against our flesh. But, Peter tells us, "By his divine power, God has given us everything we need for living a godly life" (2 Peter 1:3 NLT). And that *everything* is the indwelling of the Holy Spirit!

PONDER:

I am responsible before God for my behavior, responses
and choices. We may not be able to control the circumstances
that come into our lives, but by God's grace we can control how
we respond to the circumstances He has allowed in our lives.[91]
—Nancy DeMoss Wolgemuth

MEDITATE:

But you are not controlled by your sinful nature.
You are controlled by the Spirit if you have the Spirit of
God living in you. (And remember that those who do not have
the Spirit of Christ living in them do not belong to him at all.
Romans 8:9 NLT

PRAY:

Father, You have designed us to need the indwelling of Your Holy Spirit
in order to handle life and all that it can throw our way. Help me to be sensitive
to Your voice and allow the power that You impart to control my words, actions,
attitudes, and emotions. I long to be totally under Your Spirit's control.
Amen!

[91]Nancy DeMoss Wolgemuth, *Lies Women Believe* (Chicago, Illinois: Moody Publishers, 2001). P. 260

Day Two

Yesterday you were asked the question, *What are the things that cause you to lose your **self-control***? Below is my list, and I am guessing that many of mine appeared on your list as well. The things that can cause me to lose **self-control** are:

- When people say things that are hurtful, incorrect, or false

- When I feel pressure to please others

- When I am misunderstood

- When I am wrongfully or falsely accused

- When I think I am disappointing others

- When I cannot control a situation in which the results will reflect on me

- When I am expected somewhere by a certain time and interruptions or responsibility make me late

- When people are driving under the speed limit (I am typically very patient with most situations in life except slow drivers when I am in a hurry!)

There are probably more that the Lord will reveal to me after writing this lesson, but for now, this is an extensive enough list! In looking at these things, I realized that it is not the situation that causes me to lose **self-control**, but my flesh's response to the situation. I **choose** to allow it to cause me to lose my **self-control**.

I was speaking at a church where many of the members were women I had known for years, but had not seen in a while. During the break in the evening program, one lady approached the podium where I stood. She said, "You are still pretty, but you have really aged." I wanted to say, "Excuse me? So have you!" But I took a breath and smiled as I responded, "Yes, I have."

At that moment I had a choice to make. Thankfully, I **chose** to allow the Spirit to **control** my response. I was not really offended by what she said, because aging is a reality for all of us. I had aged in the ten years since she had seen me last.

See that no one repays anyone evil for evil,
but always seek to do good to one another and to everyone.
I Thessalonians 5:15 ESV

1. Write the definition of the word **choice**.

2. Based on the definition above, explain how **choice** relates to the discipline of **self-control**?

3. When it comes to our exercising self-control, we as Christian women can either choose our FLE__H or the H__O__Y SP__RI__

As Christians, I think one of the greatest powers we have is our **choices**, which should always involve choosing to do the right thing. When we talk about doing the right thing, we undoubtedly need to consider the word **love**. God's love for us and our love for Him should compel us to desire to do good and love as He loves. Because He first loved us, we are to love others, and we are to respond in love.

Jesus is the ultimate example of always doing the right thing. He did good everywhere he went. He lived his life to obey His Father in every way. As Christians and His children, we should likewise **choose** to do the right thing in every circumstance.

Read John 18:22-19:1, 17-37.

4. How was Jesus treated?

5. What was his response to this treatment?

Jesus **chose** to speak kindly and respectfully even in the midst of cruelty, mistreatment, and verbal attack. When it comes to the words we speak or those spoken to us, we have a **choice** in what we say and in how we respond. Will our flesh reign over our heart and mouth or will the Spirit?

*Silence is not always a sign of weakness; it is also a sign of strong **self-control**.*
—Author Unknown

6. Fill in the blanks of the following verse: "So whoever _____ the _____ thing to do and _____ to do it, for him it is _____" (James 4:17 ESV).

If we **choose** to allow our flesh to respond instead of the Spirit, we are sinning! At that point, we have lost **self-control**. Remember Peter said in 2 Peter 1 that as Christians we have His divine nature in us which gives us power over sin.

PONDER:

I am a spiritual being. After this body is dead, my spirit will soar.
I refuse to let what will rot rule the eternal. I choose self-control.
I will be drunk only by joy. I will be impassioned only by my faith.
I will be influenced only by God. I will be taught only by Christ.[92]
—Max Lucado

MEDITATE:

He will die for lack of self-control; he will be lost because of his great foolishness.
Proverbs 5:23 NLT

PRAY:

Lord, in all things we have a choice. You gave us a free will but also the Holy Spirit
to control our will—if we will allow Him that control. Help me to choose to allow the
Holy Spirit full and complete control over my thoughts, words, and actions. With Your divine
power living in me, I will have power over my flesh, controlling my responses and reactions.
Thank you that because You live in me I am able to be self-controlled.
Amen!

[92]Max Lucado, https://www.christianquotes.info/quotes-by-author/max-lucado-quotes

Day Three

Because I am the type of personality who likes to plan ahead, I tend to be a very cautious person. You would not label me as **impulsive**. Well, let me clarify, I am not **impulsive** except when it comes to ice cream and spending. In these two areas, I have to exercise **self-control**. For the next three days, we are going to look at the Biblical definition for **self-control**. That definition is *restraint exercised over one's own impulses, emotions, or desires*. We will be looking at the three areas of restraint, starting with our **impulses**.

First, let's define two of the words found within the Biblical definition of **self-control**.

Restraint: The root word of restraint is **refrain**, and it means *to hold back, limit, control, or restrict*.

Exercised: *To make active use of; employ, apply, or exert; exercise restraint; exercise control.*

In other words, in living out the Biblical definition of **self-control**, we are to maintain control over our impulses, emotions, and desires that are not honoring to or reflective of Christ.

1. How would you define **impulse** or **impulsive**?

To be **impulsive** is *to act without forethought*. Forethought is giving careful consideration of what will be necessary or may happen in the future. So, one who is **impulsive** does not consider what might happen as a result of his actions.

Years ago, when we lived in Houston, Texas, my husband, Mark, took his BMW into the dealership to be serviced. While he was waiting, he walked around the showroom floor. As he neared the front door, sitting in front of him was a brand new two door black on black coupe with a thin red stripe down the side. The sight of that beautiful little sports car was more than he could resist. That afternoon, he showed no restraint and acted without forethought. He threw **self-control** out the window, and on an **impulse**, he bought the car.

One's greatest challenge is to control one's self.
—Author Unknown

That morning Mark left with one car and returned home that evening with a different car. We gave up a large sedan for a small fast sleek two door black coupe loaded with all the horns and whistles a guy could want. Mark acted on **impulse** and did not consider what might happen as a result of his actions. Because he did, that Christmas our girls were packed in the back seat of that car like sardines as we traveled over 2000 miles to see family. Mark did not exercise restraint over his own **impulses**; he did not apply **self-control**—and our girls paid for it!

Turn to John 18:1-27 and read about a man in the Bible who had difficulty exercising restraint over his own **impulses**.

2. Who was the disciple spoken of in these verses?

3. Circle the words below that would describe an impulsive person such as Peter.

EXCITABLE	CAUTIOUS
CALM	QUICK
SWIFT	HEADSTRONG
HASTY	SLOW
CAREFUL	DELIBERATE
STEADY	SUDDEN

Peter was quick to jump into things; he dove headlong into situations. You might say he was **impulsive**. His greatest challenge was to **control** himself, his words, and actions. When something needed to be said, Peter was usually the disciple to say it. When something needed to be done, Peter was usually the one to do it. But Peter did not always count the cost of his words or his actions.

4. Peter's responses were varied—sometimes right and sometimes wrong. Below, match Peter's action with his response.

_____Matthew 16:15-16   a.) Peter was quick to say the right thing.

_____Matthew 16:21-22   b.) Peter was quick to say the wrong thing.

_____John 6:67-69   c.) Peter was quick to do the wrong thing.

_____John 18:10   d.) Peter was quick to do the right thing.

Peter was a devoted follower of Christ who had a passion for sharing the gospel, yet at times, he failed to exercise restraint over his own impulses, emotions, and desires—just like you and I do!

> *This impetuous, impulsive, temper-minded, disloyal, faithless man*
> *is the one Jesus named* **Rock**. *Jesus took Peter with all his flaws and disappointments*
> *and transformed his heart to become one of the most influential leaders in history and one*
> *of the founders of the living church. It is through Peter's call to ministry, his leadership*
> *characteristics, his faults, and his sanctification that I am reminded that God can call us*
> *to great things regardless of who we are or how far we fall.*[93] —*Seth Denney*

5. Are you **self-controlled** or **impulsive**? Give some prayerful thought to your answer. If **impulsive**, explain in what areas you are **impulsive**. List below.

Ask God to help you exercise restraint over your impulses and to exhibit the spiritual fruit of **self-control**.

Prudent cautious self-control is wisdom's root.[94]
—*Robert Burns*

6. Look up the definitions of **prudent** and **cautious**. Explain in your own words the meaning of the words of Robert Burns.

[93]Rev. Seth Denney, www.pappadenney.blogspot
[94]Robert Burns: Scottish Poet and Lyricist, https://www.azquotes.com/quote/568259

PONDER:

The weakest person is the one who has no self-control.
—Author Unknown

MEDITATE:

But I say, walk by the Spirit, and you will not carry out the desire of the flesh.
For the flesh sets its desire against the Spirit, and the Spirit against the flesh;
for these are in opposition to one another so that you may not do the things
that you please. But if you are led by the Spirit, you are not under the Law.
Galatians 5:16-18 NASB

PRAY:

Lord, like Peter, I am often impulsive when it comes to my words and my actions.
Forgive me. I am asking that You take full possession of my words, my thoughts,
my emotions, and my actions. I want to be a reflection of You Lord and do great things
for You and Your kingdom. Help me to exhibit the fruit of self-control in my life.
Amen!

Day Four

It was a full day that began with getting bloodwork done, followed by brunch with friends, and then a long *to-do* list. Since I was going to be out, I decided I would make a day of it and run my errands before returning home to write. I was at my last stop, Hobby Lobby, where I wanted to purchase a new journal.

I looked for the line with the least number of shoppers with the least amount of purchases. That is usually a safe bet and pays off—not that day! You know how tired you are after running numerous errands, getting in and out of the car all afternoon—that is how I felt. I just wanted to get my journal and go home.

The woman in front of me was purchasing a green t-shirt for a St. Patrick's Day party. She told the cashier all about where she had been to look for a shirt, why she needed it, and then asked the cashier if she thought the stickers she was purchasing would stick to the shirt. They discussed it for a few minutes, then looked at me as if to say, "What do you think?" So, I gave my opinion as to whether or not stickers would stick to a cotton t-shirt. I just wanted to get my journal and go home.

As she searched and searched for her credit card, I could feel my blood pressure going up and up. Fortunately, the way I was feeling on the inside did not show on the outside. Then the credit card machine rejected her card. The cashier had her reinsert it two more times until the machine finally accepted it. Because of the ongoing discussion about the stickers adhering to the shirt, she missed the time allotted for her signature. The cashier had to start her transaction over again. She asked the lady to slide her card down the side of the machine one more time. She did it wrong the first time, but finally got the strip turned toward the machine, and the purchase was approved. Whew!

Let's review the Biblical definition for self-control. It is restraint exercised over one's own impulses, emotions, or desires.

The longer the lady took to check out, the harder it became to **control** my emotions. Now, those around me would not have known this—it was all internal for I did not let it show. When I got in my car, I remembered, "Oh my! I am writing on **self-control**, and I couldn't even restrain my **emotions** long enough for a woman to get her questions answered and purchase her St. Patrick's day t-shirt." I had to ask God to forgive me for not **restraining** my **emotions**.

The word **emotions** is defined as *a natural instinctive state of mind deriving from one's circumstances, mood, or relationships with others.*

1. List four synonyms found in the dictionary under the definition of **emotions**?

The Bible says that we are to be controlled by the Holy Spirit—not our **emotions**. In recognizing our **emotions** and bringing them to God, we can submit ourselves to Him, allowing Him to do His cleansing work in our hearts by directing our **emotions** and actions.

2. Using the ESV Bible, summarize what the following verses say about the Holy Spirit's control.

ROMANS 8:7-11

1 CORINTHIANS 3:16

EPHESIANS 3:16

EPHESIANS 5:15–18

Women are emotional beings, yet we cannot use that as an excuse for ungodly behavior. When we become born again believers, we are filled with the Holy Spirit, and God wants us to allow His Spirit total control over our **emotions**.

> *Better to be patient than powerful; better to have **self-control** than to conquer a city.*
> *Proverbs 16:32 NLT*

> *Real contentment must come from within. You and I cannot change or **control***
> *the world around us, but we can change and **control** the world within us.*[95]
> *—Warren Wiersbe*

I gave full reign to my **emotions** as I stood in line at Hobby Lobby that day. I did not allow the Holy Spirit dominance over my thoughts or **emotions**. I could not change or control the circumstances around me, but I could have changed and controlled the circumstances within me!

[95]Warren Wiersbe, http://www.searchquotes.com/search/Self Control Christian/#ixzz6F7sbzrPT

PONDER:

After this body is dead, my spirit will soar ... I will be impassioned only by my faith. I will be influenced only by God. I will be taught only by Christ.[96]
—Max Lucado

MEDITATE:

Then he said to me, This is the word of the Lord to Zerubbabel: Not by might, nor by power, but by my Spirit, says the Lord of hosts.
Zechariah 4:6 ESV

PRAY:

Father, You made me as a woman with emotions, but help me to not allow my emotions to control my responses. You have placed Your powerful presence through the Holy Spirit within each believer. May I allow Him indwelling and abundant control over my thoughts, words, actions, and emotions.
Amen!

[96]Max Lucado, https://www.christianquotes.info/quotes-by-topic/quotes-about-self-control

Day Five

It was a fun evening as my daughter and family came over for dinner joining with my niece and family who were in town. As we finished dinner, the children were becoming restless knowing that dessert, a homemade chocolate chip cookie ice cream sandwich, awaited them. The parents cleaned the kitchen as I prepared the dessert. The little ones eyes were bulging as they gazed at the ice cream sandwiches. Micah, who was 4, could hardly wait for his ice cream sandwich. His dad reached for a plate and a knife to cut Micah's cookie in half. Micah quickly said, "No. That is mine." His dad responded, "This is too big. You will need to half it with your brother." Micah began to get upset at the thought of having to share his ice cream sandwich. With tears forming in the corners of his eyes, he said, "But, I wanted that. I wanted that."

The Bible definition of **desire** is *a conscious impulse toward something that promises enjoyment or satisfaction in its attainment, longing, craving.*

Micah **desired** the homemade chocolate chip ice cream sandwich, and he **desired** it for himself. He had a conscious impulse toward that ice cream sandwich that promised enjoyment and satisfaction. That **desire** was a natural **desire**; he longed to have the entire sandwich to himself.

Amy Carmichael said of **desire**, "I pray Thee hush the hurrying, eager longing, I pray Thee soothe the pangs of keen **desire**—See in my quiet places, wishes thronging—Forbid them, Lord, purge, though it be with fire."[97]

God created us with natural **desires**. These **desires** were meant to serve good and healthy purposes. As human beings, we have a desire for love, food, rest, sleep, and companionship. The problem occurs when we fail to channel our **desires** in the right direction.

A good example of this is found in the book of Genesis. After creating the earth and all that was to dwell upon it, God created the first man and named him Adam. Read Genesis 2:4-7.

God created a garden (a home) for Adam to live in called Eden. It was a place where all Adam's **desires** would be met. He was well fed and well cared for in the garden. God gave Adam responsibility for the garden; he was the caretaker.

Read Genesis 2:15-17. God gave Adam one commandment to abide by, one restriction, if you will.

    1.   What was that restriction?

God did not physically prevent Adam from eating from the tree, but rather gave him a choice and thus the possibility of choosing wrongly.

[97]Amy Carmichael, www.christian-living, god-s-will-prayer

All of Adam's needs and **desires** were met in the garden except for human companionship. Read Genesis 2:18-25.

2. How did God meet Adam's human **desire** for companionship?

Satan targeted Eve. Let's look at how he deceived her. His process of deception was very clear:

- He twisted God's Word to cause doubt as to God's goodness.

- He implied that God is stingy, not wanting to share with Eve His knowledge of good and evil.

- He caused her to forget all God had done for her and instead focus on what He had forbidden.

- He told her that she could become more like God by defying God's authority, by taking God's place and deciding for herself what is best for her life.

- He appealed to her fleshly **desires**.

> *The woman was convinced (she believed the lie). She saw that the tree was beautiful and its fruit looked delicious, and she wanted the wisdom it would give her. So, she took some of the fruit and ate it. Then she gave some to her husband, who was with her, and he ate it, too.*
> *Genesis 3:6 NLT*

Read Deuteronomy 30:15-16.

3. What choice is given?

4. What commandment is given?

5. What promise is given as a result of obedience?

God gives us a choice, just as He did Adam and Eve. We can choose to allow our flesh to control our **desires**, or we can choose to allow God control over our **desires**. We must learn to choose the correct response to our God-given **desires** based on His Word, or we will suffer the consequences.

6. Read Genesis 3:7, 16-24. What were the consequences of Adam and Eve's wrong response to their **desire** to be like God?

Let's review the Biblical definition for self-control.
It is restraint exercised over one's own impulses, emotions, or desires.

7. Fill in the following blanks: "But I say, _____ by the _____, and you will _____ gratify the _____ of the flesh" (Galatians 5:16 ESV).

God created us with impulses, emotions, and **desires**. Each one in itself is not bad if placed under the Holy Spirit's control. Any one of these outside the Spirit's control can have devastating results.

Let's take the natural **desire** for love as an example. If your **desire** for love has been placed under the Spirit's control, it will remain a pure love. But, if your desire is under the control of your flesh, it most likely will become an impure and a defiled love.

8. Write the definition of the word **defile**.

9. Write the definition of the word **impure**.

Let's look at an example of a man whose desire
was not under the Holy Spirit's control.

Read 2 Samuel 13:1-21. What we see in this story is a **desire** under the control of the flesh and the result of it.

- The **desire** Amnon thought was love was really lust.

- He claimed to be in love but was actually overcome with lust.

- Under the Spirit's control love is patient, kind, and does not seek its own way.

- Without the Spirit's control, what is thought to be love is lust, and lust is not patient nor kind, but seeks to have its own way.

- Love is controlled, and lust in uncontrolled.

- Love focuses on the other person; lust focuses on self.

10. Amnon was focused on his needs, his **desires**, and lost sight of the proper path. What were the devastating results of Amnon's **desires**?

The more focused you are on yourself, the more
distracted you will be from the proper path.[98]
— John MacArthur

[98]John MacArthur, https://www.christianquotes.info/quotes-by-author/john-macarthur-quotes, July 2015

PONDER:

Outside of Christ, I am weak; in Christ, I am strong.[99]
—Watchman Nee

MEDITATE:

So prepare your minds for action and exercise self-control.
1 Peter 1:13a NLT

PRAY:

Lord, I am asking that You take control of my desires.
May they reflect Your character and not my ugly flesh. My desires
can only remain pure if under Your Spirit's control. May Your love,
Father, exude from my life as I allow You total and
complete dominance in my heart and life.
Amen!

[99]Watchman Nee, www.christianquotes.com/selfcontrol/wtachmannee

Week Seven Menu

Chicken Enchilada Rice Casserole

3 cups cooked chicken breasts, shredded

2 cups dry Basmati or brown rice

2 (10 ounce) cans Enchilada sauce (or homemade)

1 (16 ounce) can refried or black beans

1 cup white Cheddar, shredded, divided

1 cup Monterey Jack cheese, shredded, divided

1 (14½ ounce) can corn, drained

1 jalapeño, chopped

Salt and pepper to taste

Preheat oven to 350°F. Cook the rice according the package instructions. Mix the two cheeses together. In a large bowl mix the shredded chicken with the enchilada sauce, refried beans, and half of the cheese. Add rice, season with salt and pepper if needed, and mix well. Pour rice mixture into a large casserole dish. Top with corn then with remainder of cheese. Bake for 30 to 40 minutes or until cheese melts and is bubbly.

ENCHILADA SAUCE:

¼ cup canola oil

2 tablespoons flour

2 tablespoons chili powder

1 (8 ounce) can tomato sauce

1 teaspoon salt

1½ cups low-sodium chicken broth

½ teaspoon ground cumin

1 teaspoon garlic powder

½ teaspoon onion powder

Heat oil in a large skillet to medium heat. Whisk in flour and chili powder. Reduce heat to medium and continue to whisk until lightly browned. Gradually whisk in tomato sauce, salt, chicken broth, cumin, garlic powder, and onion powder. Stir until smooth, and continue simmering over medium heat about 10 minutes, or until slightly thickened. Serve immediately or keep covered in bowl in the refrigerator for up to 3 days.

CORN AND BLACK BEAN SALSA:

Use 2 cups of your favorite salsa. Cook two ears of fresh corn on the cob and once cooled, remove the kernels from the cob, and add to salsa. Drain and rinse 1 cup of black beans. Mix thoroughly with salsa and corn until well blended. Serve with your favorite chips. Note: Canned or frozen corn may be used.

Sour Cream Cornbread

¼ cup butter, softened

3 tablespoons sugar

2 eggs, slightly beaten

½ cup sour cream

½ cup milk

1 cup all-purpose flour

⅔ cup plain cornmeal

1½ teaspoons baking powder

½ teaspoon salt

¼ teaspoon baking soda

Preheat oven to 425°F. Combine butter and sugar in small bowl. Beat at medium speed, scraping bowl often, until creamy. Add eggs, one at a time, beating well after each addition. Stir in sour cream and milk. Add all remaining ingredients. Reduce speed to low; beat just until mixed. Pour batter into greased 8-inch cast-iron skillet, or 8-inch greased square baking pan. Bake 18 to 22 minutes. For a cast iron skillet, bake 22 to 24 minutes or until golden brown and toothpick inserted in center comes out clean. Serve warm.

Baked Cinnamon Chips with Fruit Salsa

1 peach or nectarine, peeled and diced

3 kiwis, peeled and diced

1 (16 ounce) package strawberries, hulled and diced

1 mango, peeled, cored, and diced

1½ teaspoons fresh lemon juice

2 tablespoons strawberry jam

CINNAMON CHIPS:

¼ cup granulated sugar

6 (6-inch) flour tortillas

1 teaspoon cinnamon

2 tablespoons butter, melted

Preheat oven to 400°F. Coat baking sheet with non-stick cooking spray and set aside. In a large mixing bowl, toss together peach, mango, kiwi, strawberries, lemon juice, and strawberry jam. Chill salsa. In a small bowl mix sugar and cinnamon. Brush both sides of the tortillas lightly with melted butter. Sprinkle each side of the tortillas evenly with cinnamon and sugar mixture. Cut tortillas into wedges with pizza cutter. Transfer to prepared baking sheet in a single layer. Bake 10 to 12 minutes, turning chips over halfway through. Let chips cool then serve with salsa.

SHORT-CUTS...

- **CHICKEN ENCHILADA RICE CASSEROLE:** Chicken Enchilada Rice Casserole: This dish can be prepared days ahead (minus the cheese for topping) and frozen. Remove from freezer the morning before serving and store in refrigerator until time to bake. Top with cheese and bake according to directions.

- **ENCHILADA SAUCE:** Can be made up to 3 days prior to serving/using in recipe. Just reheat and place in casserole recipe.

- **SALSA WITH CORN AND BLACK BEANS:** Best prepared 2 to 4 hours prior to serving.

- **SOUR CREAM CORNBREAD:** This recipe can be made ahead of time and reheated but best hot out of the oven.

- **FRUIT SALSA WITH BAKED CINNAMON SUGAR CHIPS:** Salsa is best prepared and chilled 2 to 4 hours prior to serving. Chips can be made the day before but should be stored in zipper-lock bag or air-tight container.

HEALTHY TIPS...

- **CHICKEN ENCHILADA RICE CASSEROLE:** Using homemade Enchilada sauce will be more healthy than store bought brands with preservatives.

- **CHICKEN ENCHILADA RICE CASSEROLE:** Black beans are a much healthier choice than refried beans.

- **CHICKEN ENCHILADA RICE CASSEROLE:** Fresh or frozen corn is healthier than canned corn.

- **CHICKEN ENCHILADA RICE CASSEROLE:** Reduce cheese to half the amount called for or, if you are dairy intolerant, purchase dairy-free cheese.

- **ENCHILADA SAUCE:** Made in Italy *Cento* brand tomato products are additive free. *Found at Walmart and other local grocers.

- **ENCHILADA SAUCE:** Use organic chicken broth with no additives. Flour can be replaced with gluten free thickeners. Almond flour can successfully replace white flour in most recipes measurement for measurement. You can even make your own almond flour from whole nuts. Due to the high fat content of the almond flour, making it fresh when you need it prevents the flour from becoming rancid in storage.

- **SALSA WITH CORN AND BLACK BEANS:** Purchase organic Salsa and one with the least preservatives.

- **SOUR CREAM CORNBREAD:** Flour can be replaced with gluten free flours. Almond flour can successfully replace white flour in most recipes measurement for measurement.

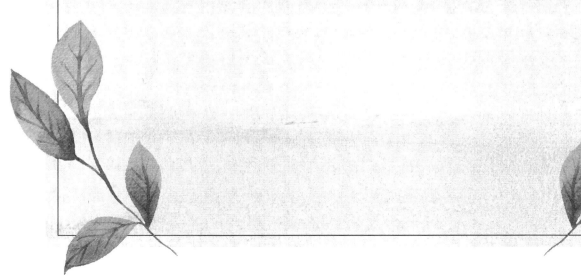

Worry

The beginning of anxiety is the end of faith, and the beginning of true faith is the end of anxiety.

—George Mueller

*O*ur younger daughter invited me to go with her family on spring break to Phoenix, Arizona, for baseball spring training. Our grandsons are huge Texas Rangers fans. As the time grew closer to drive to Texas and then fly on to Phoenix, I found myself feeling a bit anxious. I am not typically what you would describe as a *worrier* or an *anxious* person. That is not my normal response to life—just to flying! Let me mention here that heights scare the daylights out of me! So, if you want to get my blood pressure up, just book a flight to any destination, and my blood pressure will sky rocket; no pun intended! It was not the germs that seem to grow within the body of an airplane that made me anxious or worried —just flying itself. The takeoff, landing, height, and turbulence make me quite anxious, other than that I am fine with it!

As we boarded the plane, I was observing my grandchildren. They were so excited about the week to come and all the opportunities they would have to watch some of their very favorite players. If they were **worried** or **anxious**, it sure did not show. I wanted to remain as calm as they were and not let the anxiety that was swelling inside me show. In the years prior to Mark's illness, we flew quite a lot. He loved to fly, but was always aware of my concern about flying. He would sweetly encourage me that everything was going to be fine; there was no need to worry. I remember on several flights grabbing his leg at the knee when turbulence would occur. He was very kind without looking up from his book, he would just pat my hand as if to say, "Everything is fine; you don't need to be **anxious**." Can I just tell you that it is not appropriate to grab the knee of a strange man sitting to your right should turbulence occur during a flight! After Mark passed away, I only made that mistake once!

So, what is the root of **anxiety** and **worry**? I think it stems from not having **control** over our circumstances, i.e., flying, illness, life, others, etc. We all like to have some degree of **control** over our lives, but when we do not—we become **anxious**. Have you ever observed people sitting in a dentist office? Many are **anxious** about what is going to happen and the fact that it is out of their control.

Watchman Nee said, "An unpeaceful mind cannot operate normally."[100]

When we are **anxious** and **worried**, we cannot think clearly—like grabbing the knee of a stranger on a flight! The Apostle Paul tells us to be **anxious** for nothing. But, is that possible? It must be, or God would not have written it in His Word. Have you ever noticed that in God's Word, He never gives us a directive without giving us the process in which to accomplish it?

> *Don't worry about anything; instead, pray about everything. Tell God what you need, and thank him for all he has done. Then you will experience God's peace, which exceeds anything we can understand. His peace will guard your hearts and minds as you live in Christ Jesus.*
> *Philippians 4:6-7 NLT*

God is saying, why are you **anxious** and **worried**? I said never to worry. But, when you do, remember to turn to Me, trust Me with every detail that is concerning you, thank Me, and I will watch over you, direct you, protect you, provide for you, and give you peace. No worries!

[100]Watchman Nee, https://quotefancy.com/quote/932056/Watchman-Nee

Day One

I am writing this week's lesson in the midst of the most anxious time that I can remember in my lifetime, apart from 9/11. Things appear to be totally out of control, and people are worried and anxious. Some media sources are daily throwing gasoline on the fire of fear. Many Christians are fearing when they should be trusting, **worrying** when they should be exhibiting a spirit of peace, hoarding when they should be sharing, and criticizing those in authority when they should be praying for them.

1. Write the definition of the word **worry**.

2. Write the definition of the word **anxiety**.

Our lack of control over the circumstances happening around us can cause **worry** and **anxiety**.

COVID-19 created an environment where decisions concerning our jobs, education, and lives were being made that we had no control over; thus fear set in. Early on, I received a phone call from a lady relating details of what might happen that left me shaking and my heart rate climbing. Once I calmed down and remembered that God is sovereign and in control, even if it does not look like it, my heart rate slowed and I stopped shaking. I went to bed reading scripture, listening to praise music, and praying as I fell asleep. I slept through the night resting in Him.

3. Write two verses below that instruct us to **rest** in the Lord:

1 :

2 :

To **rest** is *to cease work or movement, to relax, refresh oneself, slow down, pause, or cease to engage in strenuous or stressful activity for a period.*

Resting is the opposite of **worry** and **anxiety**! When we **rest** in Christ, we have peace and a calm demeanor that others will notice—especially in uncertain times.

I was reading through Psalm 23 before going to bed one evening and thinking about rest. The Psalm says, "The Lord is my shepherd; I shall not want. He makes me lie down in green pastures. He leads me beside still waters. He restores my soul. He leads me in paths of righteousness for His name's sake. Even though I walk through the valley of the shadow of death, I will fear no evil, for You are with me; Your rod and Your staff, they comfort me. You prepare a table before me in the presence of my enemies; you anoint my head with oil; my cup overflows. Surely goodness and mercy shall follow me all the days of my life, and I shall dwell in the house of the Lord forever" (Psalm 23 ESV).

> *Many of David's psalms are full of complaints, but this is full of comforts,*
> *and the expressions of delight in God's great goodness and our dependence upon him.*[101]
> —*Matthew Henry*

Let's look closer at this Psalm:

- The Psalmist says the Lord is my shepherd, meaning He is a personal Shepherd, shepherding the sheep under His care.

- He **makes** us lie down. Obviously, God knew our human tendency to resist **rest**, so he has to **make** us lie down—He orchestrates our circumstances so we will lie down and **rest**.

- He **restores** our souls, because He is the only source of true restoration.

- He **leads** us in paths of righteousness for His name sake. Because we are fleshly beings, we are prone to wander away from righteousness. So, we need Him to lead us for our good and His glory.

- He **comforts** us in uncertain times; therefore, we have no reason to fear.

- He has made preparation for all we need—both for life and godliness. All He has **given** us, He **gives** in abundance. We have bountiful provision for our bodies and our souls, for the life that now is, and for that which is to come. We are His anointed. His power and His presence lives within us.

- Surely goodness and mercy shall **follow** us all the days of our lives, and we shall dwell in the house of the Lord forever. This is our hope in troubled times. His goodness and His mercy are with us 24/7, 365 days a year!

The words in **bold** above are verbs and convey an action, occurrence, or state of being.

This says to me that the Lord **makes** us, **leads** us, **comforts** us, **gives** to us, and **prepares** for us what we need—He is the One who **initiates**, **activates**, and **accomplishes** each of these occurrences in our lives.

[101]Matthew Henry, https://www.biblestudytools.com/commentaries/matthew-henry- complete/psalms/23.html

4. A verb needs a noun. In case you have forgotten, a noun is a person, place, or thing. So, what are the nouns in Psalm 23:1?

He is **Lord** over our lives, so we can **rest** in knowing that we don't have to **worry** or be **anxious** because nothing can touch us that has not been permitted by the **Lord our Shepherd**.

5. What does 1 Peter 5:7 tell us to do with our worries and our cares?

I received the following song through a text from a friend. I have listened to it numerous times. I truly believe worshiping through music calms our hearts and spirits, taking us to the Father who tenderly shepherds us with His love, assurance, and care. In times when we are faced with worrisome and **anxious** circumstances, may we turn our eyes to Him and find rest!

> *Turn your eyes upon Jesus. Look full in His wonderful face, and the things*
> *of earth will grow strangely dim in the light of His glory and grace.*
>
> *Turn your eyes to the hillside where justice and mercy embraced,*
> *there the Son of God gave His life for us and our measureless debt was erased.*
>
> *Jesus to You we lift up our eyes, Jesus our glory and our prize. We adore You,*
> *behold You, our Savior ever true. Oh, Jesus we turn our eyes to You.*
>
> *Turn your eyes to the morning and see Christ the lion awake, what a glorious dawn,*
> *fear of death is gone for we carry His life in our veins.*
>
> *Jesus to You we lift up our eyes, Jesus our glory and our prize. We adore You,*
> *behold You, our Savior ever true. Oh, Jesus we turn our eyes to You.*
>
> *Turn your eyes to the heavens, our King will return for His own and every knee will bow,*
> *every tongue will shout, all glory to Jesus alone.*
>
> *Oh, Jesus we turn our eyes to You. Jesus to You we lift our eyes,*
> *our glory and our prize. We adore You, behold You, our Savior ever true.*
> *Oh, Jesus we turn our eyes to You. Oh, Jesus we turn our eyes to You.*[102]

[102]Sovereign Grace Music, *Turn Your Eyes Upon Jesus,* © 2019 Sovereign Grace Worship (ASCAP)/
Sovereign Grace Praise (BMI)/Sovereign Grace Songs (SESAC)

PONDER:

Our rest lies in looking to the Lord, not to ourselves.[103]
—Watchman Nee

MEDITATE:

My peace I leave with you; my peace I give you. I do not give to you as the world gives.
Do not let your hearts be troubled and do not be afraid.
John 14:27

PRAY:

Lord, I look to You and seek Your presence. You are the only true source of peace and joy
in a world of worry and anxiety. Thank you for giving me rest in the midst of uncertainty,
faith instead of fear, and calm in the midst of chaos. You are a loving, faithful,
ever-present Shepherd, who watches over His sheep, of which I am one—for that I am thankful.
Amen!

[103]Watchman Nee, https://quotefancy.com/quote/932012/Watchman-Nee-Our-rest-lies-in-looking-to-the-Lord.

Day Two

While talking to a Christian gentleman who frequents my gym, I mentioned about a conversation I had with my granddaughter. She was **fearful** after listening to adults who were talking about nothing but COVID-19. She just needed to be encouraged and reassured that all was going to be fine. My gym friend responded that he had witnessed more **fear** in the adults than the children. I shared my testimony with him; "Mike, when Mark (my husband) was first diagnosed with Multiple Systems Atrophy (a rare and degenerative neurological disease), I lived in **fear** for a time. It was miserable! But, God clearly showed me that **fear** and faith cannot coexist. One or the other will have dominance over your emotions. **Fear** is of the enemy. If Satan can cause us to live in **fear**, we will live in a state of hopelessness. **Fear** grips and debilitates—it renders us helpless and hopeless! I refuse to live that way! Especially when I don't have to. I serve an all-powerful Sovereign God." He agreed!

If we truly believe God is sovereign over our lives, the world, and the pandemic, then we are neither helpless nor hopeless. The problem we face is that we live in a culture that has sold people on the philosophy that they can control their own happiness, future, and ultimately their destiny. But you can't! And the result of that false teaching is becoming evident, causing people to panic and live **fearful** lives. They have no control, but then they never really did—they just thought they did. God created the earth, and He controls the earth. God created you, and He is sovereign over your life and mine.

If you have accepted Him as your Lord and Savior and are living for Him and not yourself, there is good news—you have nothing to **fear**! You serve a God who can be trusted. Exercise your **faith** and **trust** Him. Then you will experience **peace** and **rest**, for He is a God of **peace** and **rest**. He can be **trusted** with every aspect of your life.

1. Write the definition of the word **fear**.

2. List a few synonyms for **fear** below.

3. Do any of these words describe the way you are living? **Yes**_____ **No**_____. Explain.

4. Fill in the blanks for the following verses on **fear**: "When I am _____, I put my _____ in you. In God, whose word I praise—in God I trust and am not _____. What can mere mortals do to me?" (Psalm 56:3-4 NIV).

"So do not _____, for I am with you; do not be dismayed, for I am your God. I _____ strengthen you and _____ you; I _____ uphold you with _____ righteous right hand" (Isaiah 41:10 NIV).

"For God has _____ given us a spirit of _____ and timidity, but of _____, love, and self-discipline" (2 Timothy 1:7 NLT).

5. Summarize below what God tells us in the above verses related to **fear**.

Living in a state of worry and anxiety is a **choice**. When worry and anxiety dominates our thoughts and actions, we are **choosing** to allow them full reign over our emotions. In doing so, it robs us of **joy** and **peace**. In addition, our **fear** will bring about **fear** in others—as the lady's call did for me. Just as all viruses are contagious, so are worry, anxiety, and **fear**. We can affect others with our deadly spirit of worry, anxiety, and **fear**.

I have found Watchman Nee's quote from our Introduction to be very true. When my mind is not peaceful, I cannot operate normally—I am worried, anxious, and **fearful**. If I dwell on difficulty or feel uneasy about an imminent event or something with an uncertain outcome, I cannot have a mind or body at peace. God offers you and me rest and peace, if we will receive it. After all, He is the God of both.

6. Write the verse on **peace** found in Psalm 4:8.

7. Write the verse on **rest** found in Matthew 11:28.

In the New American Standard Bible the phrase *do not fear* appears 57 times and *do not be afraid* appears 46 times. God knew our human tendency would be to become **fearful**, so He provided the reassurance we would need in His Word. We as Christians are to exhibit a spirit of **peace**, **rest**, and **hope** during turbulent times.

COVID-19 will pass, and life will resume. Hopefully, not as it was, but with a new perspective on life and the blessings we enjoy. May we be more thoughtful of those around us, more giving, more helpful, more loving, more restful, more in love with Jesus and more at **peace**—less worrisome and anxious—because we serve a God who can be **trusted**. Your next crisis may not be a pandemic, but hard times will come. Our challenge is to actively trust God regardless of our circumstances.

PONDER:

If God be our God, He will give us peace in trouble.
When there is a storm without, He will make peace within. The world
can create trouble in peace, but God can create peace in trouble.[104]
—Thomas Watson

MEDITATE:

You will keep in perfect peace those whose minds are steadfast, because they trust in you.
Isaiah 26:3 NIV

PRAY:

Father, I am so thankful that You give peace in place of worry and
rest in place of anxiety. You can be trusted in all of life's circumstances.
Lord, You are an infinite source of peace and rest. Remove any spirit of
anxiety and worry within me. Stretch my faith and deepen my level of trust.
Help me to lie down in peace tonight knowing that You are a Sovereign
and trustworthy God—I have nothing to fear.
Amen!

[104]Thomas Watson, https://www.christianquotes.info/quotes-by-author/thomas-watson-quotes

Day Three

One night during the second full week of the COVID-19 scare, I fell asleep around 11:30 and woke at 1:30. I ended up tossing and turning for quite a while. I finally surmised that God must have awakened me for a reason. Have you ever felt that way? Being tired, you know you should be able to go back to sleep, but you cannot. Finally, I said, "Okay God do you have something You want to say to me? There must be a reason I cannot go back to sleep." When we ask—He is faithful to answer!

I felt the Lord saying that I was still harboring a **worrisome** and **anxious** spirit about the virus, my finances, and my future. I truly felt that I had given this to Him, but obviously I had not or He would not have awakened me in the middle of the night. As I lay there in the dark confessing my **anxiety** that was hidden deep in my heart, I pledged to **trust** him wholeheartedly.

As human beings, we can only see one another from the outside in, but God sees us from the inside out. We can hide our feelings and emotions from others, allowing them to see only what we want them to see—but we cannot hide anything from God! He knows us intimately—nothing is hidden from Him. God knew that in the deep recesses of my heart I was **worrisome** and **anxious** about the circumstances. I was **fearful**. I lacked **faith**, **trust**, **rest**, and **peace** in Him.

Jeremiah 16:17 says of God, "My eyes are on all their ways; they are not hidden from me, nor is their sin concealed from my eyes."

Nothing is hidden from God! He knows what lies in the deepest recesses of our hearts.

1. Write Hebrews 4:13 in the ICB below.

---

*When the word of God exposes our weakness and unbelief like this,
it demonstrates its inherent power, sharpness, and accuracy.[105]
—David Guzik*

If we go on to read in Hebrews 4:14-16, we will see Paul's encouraging words to all believers.

"We have a great high priest who has gone into heaven. He is Jesus the Son of God. So let us hold on to the faith we have. For our high priest is able to understand our weaknesses. He was tempted in every way that we are, but he did not sin. Let us, then, feel free to come before God's throne. Here there is grace. And we can receive mercy and grace to help us when we need it" (ICB).

Jesus, the Son of God, is both divine and compassionate. He understands that you and I are weak.

He knows that we often choose doubt over **trust**, fear over **faith**, worry over **peace**, and anxiety over **rest**. Because of that, He made a way for us to receive forgiveness, grace, and mercy through His Son's death on the cross. He can be trusted!

2. Write the definition of the word **trust**.

If we truly believe in, count on, and **trust** Him to meet our every need, we will not allow worry, anxiety, or fear to have a foothold in our lives.

In the darkness of night, God spoke, making it clear that I was not completely resting on or trusting in Him.

Jeremiah 17:10 says, "I the Lord search the heart ..." God searches the heart of every man and woman to see if we will **trust** Him (NIV).

3. Has there ever been a time when God woke you in the night to show you an area of your life in which you were not **trusting** Him? Explain below.

---

*Until you make hearing from God a priority, your ears will hear the **distractions** of the world.*
—*Author Unknown*

How easy it is for us to **worry** and be **anxious**, listening to the voices around us—the **distractions** of the world. I was allowing those **distractions**, i.e., the voices of others and social media, to rob me of the complete surrender of my **worry, anxiety,** and **fear** to the One who is fully capable of carrying the weight of them.

4. Fill in the following blanks of Nahum 1:7 from the NKJV: "The Lord is _____, a _____ in the day of _____; and he _____ those who _____ in Him."

PONDER:

God never promises to remove us from our struggles.
He does promise, however, to change the way we look at them.[106]
—Thomas Watson

MEDITATE:

But as for me, I trust in You, O Lord; I say, 'You are my God.'
Psalm 31:14 NKJV

PRAY:

Father, You know me from the inside out and yet You love me!
Like David, I am asking You to search my heart and show me any wicked
way in me and lead me in the way of everlasting. Lord, You are the only
One I can trust when life seems to be off track and beyond my control.
Thank you for being my trust, my strength, and my stronghold.
Amen!

[106]Max Lucado, https://www.beliefnet.com/quotes/christian/m/max-lucado/god-never-promises-to-remove

Day Four

My grandchildren who live in town sent a text asking if they could come spend the night. I think they needed some sense of normal. With the COVID-19 scare, schools out, and the constant barrage of people on social media calling this the end times, they needed to have fun and escape from the concerns of the week. They needed a break, and I welcomed the company! We purchased an extra-large pizza, ice cream, and settled in for the evening. The girls wanted to play *Scategories* and have a competition to see which team would win. There was much laughter as the names of things were placed in categories that were what I called a stretch as to whether or not they truly fit in that category. For instance, is an airplane a machine? One said yes, and the rest of us said no. Come to find out, according to the definition of a machine, an airplane is a machine! *Duck Duck Go* came in quite handy for verifying the validity of the answers we placed in each category.

I think the greatest laughter came from hearing the **excuses** we all gave for the answers that were a stretch. We were trying to **justify** our answers with any **excuse** we could think of and all the while trying to win. **Excuses** are nothing new. They have been around for hundreds of years.

- Eve tried to **excuse** her behavior by blaming the serpent and Adam.

- Adam tried to **excuse** his behavior by blaming Eve.

- David used the **excuse** of taking a census of the troops in order to find out how many there were. But in reality, he did it so he could take pride in the strength of his army.

Each of these made an **excuse** as to why they responded the way they did to their circumstances. There are two natural human responses to the uncertain circumstances of life, and usually we choose one of the two:

When disaster strikes, we usually respond in one of two ways. We either turn to God and enter a new relationship with Him shaped by a fuller understanding of His nature and character, or we turn away from God and blame Him or others for our troubles.[107] *NLT Parallel Study Bible*

1. Write the definition of the word **excuses**.

[107]*NLT Parallel Study Bible* (Carol Stream, Illinois: Tyndale House Publishing, 2011). P.1591

2. Write the definition of the word **blame**.

3. How have you responded when financial change, sickness, pain, heartache, or disaster has occurred in your life? Have you made **excuses** or **blamed** God and others for your responses? Explain below how you have responded and what changes you need to make.

Being fearful, as I am sure Eve, Adam, and David, were when God confronted them about their sin, does not **justify** blaming others or making **excuses** for our behavior. Let's look at a man in the Old Testament who was fearful, yet trusted God.

In 2 Chronicles 20, King Jehoshaphat was fearful due to the news of attack by three of his enemies. Although he was fearful, Jehoshaphat called on the people to fast and led them in a prayer.

He prayed. "O Lord, God of our ancestors, you alone are the God who is in heaven. You are ruler of all the kingdoms of the earth. You are powerful and mighty; no one can stand against you! O our God, did you not drive out those who lived in this land when your people Israel arrived? And did you not give this land forever to the descendants of your friend Abraham? Your people settled here and built this Temple to honor your name. They said, 'Whenever we are faced with any calamity such as war, plague, or famine, we can come to stand in your presence before this Temple where your name is honored. We can cry out to you to save us, and you will hear us and rescue us. We are powerless against this mighty army that is about to attack us. We do not know what to do, but we are looking to you for help" (2 Chronicles 20:6-9,12).

As all the men of Judah stood before the Lord, the Spirit of the Lord came upon one of the men named Jahaziel and he said,

- "**Listen**, all you people of Judah and Jerusalem! **Listen**, King Jehoshaphat!

- This is what the Lord says: Do not be **afraid**! Don't be **discouraged** by this mighty army, for the battle is not yours, but God's.

- Tomorrow, **march** out against them. But you **will not even need to fight**.

- **Take** your positions; then **stand still** and watch the Lord's victory.

- He is **with** you, O people of Judah and Jerusalem.

- Do not be **afraid** or **discouraged**.

- **Go out** against them tomorrow, for the Lord is **with you**!"

Humbled by God's words, King Jehoshaphat and the people bowed their faces to the ground and worshiped the Lord. The next morning, on the way to battle, Jehoshaphat stopped and said, "Listen to me, all you people of Judah and Jerusalem! **Believe** in the Lord your God, and you will be able to stand firm. **Believe** in his prophets, and you will succeed" (2 Chronicles 20:20 NLT).

The king appointed singers to walk ahead of the army, singing to the Lord and praising Him. This is what they sang: Give thanks to the Lord; His faithful love endures forever!

Do you know what happened next? The very moment they began to sing and worship God, He caused their enemies to fight among themselves, destroying one another. The chapter ends with these words: "So Jehoshaphat's kingdom was at **peace**, for his God had given him **rest** on every side" (2 Chronicles 20:30 NLT).

4. Fill in the blanks of the following verse:"You will keep in perfect _____ those whose _____ are steadfast, because they _____ in you" (Isaiah 26:3 NIV).

5. If your response to life's circumstances has been to make **excuses**, blame others, or to worry and be anxious, write a prayer of repentance below. God knows you and sees your responses. He asks that you confess your sin of making excuses, blaming others, and worry by **trusting** Him and allowing Him to fill you with peace.

King Jehoshaphat did not make **excuses** or blame God for his circumstances. I am certain he was somewhat anxious about it, after all, it says he was **fearful**. But, he did not allow **worry, anxiety**, or **fear** to master his emotions. Instead, he led the people in prayer, fasting, and worship—a sign of his trust in God's ability to deliver them.

Fear is a natural response to **worry** and **anxiety**. When I travel over extremely high bridges or fly in an airplane, I am **fearful**. At that point, I have a choice of what to do with my **fear**. I can make **excuses** for it, allow it to dominate my emotions, let it render me feeling helpless and hopeless, or give it to God and allow Him to fill me with **peace** as **I trust Him**.

PONDER:

The presence of fear does not mean you have no faith. Fear visits everyone.
But make your fear a visitor and not a resident.[108]
—Max Lucado

MEDITATE:

Be strong and courageous, do not be afraid or tremble at them, for the LORD
your God is the one who goes with you He will not fail you or forsake you.
Deuteronomy 31:6 NASB

PRAY:

Father, my responses to life's circumstances have not always been
honoring to You. I have often made excuses and blamed others
for my behavior. I have allowed fear to reign and rule over my emotions.
Help me to be strong in the face of fear not allowing it a foothold in
my heart and life. Thank you for promising to keep me in perfect
peace if my heart and mind are stayed on You.
Amen!

[108]Max Lucado, https://faithit.com/25-max-lucado-quotes-encourage-inspire/

Day Five

Can I just tell you that the first few weeks of the pandemic of COVID-19 were a **distraction** that defined my life. Why? Because I chose to allow it to do so. I was talking with our older daughter and we both expected to accomplish a great deal because the stores were closed and there was little to do—but neither of us did. It was as if a cloud of **worry**, **anxiety**, and **fear** were hanging over us. Something in us kicked into "survival mode," and the preparations for what "might" happen were all-consuming. Every time I passed a grocery store I found myself thinking I should stop and get a few more things—even though my refrigerator and pantry shelves were full. I didn't stop, but I felt that I should. **Worry** and **anxiety** robbed me of being productive, and kept me from leaning hard into Jesus and **trusting** Him in the midst of uncertainty.

> *The way we deal with uncertainty says a lot about whether*
> *Jesus is ahead of us leading, or behind us just carrying our stuff.*[109]
> —Bob Goff

I don't know about you, but in the uncertainty of life, I have at times chosen to place Jesus behind me instead of **trusting** Him to lead me. I have left Him in my frantic dust of **worry**, **anxiety**, and **fear**!

1. What is it about times of uncertainty that cause us to respond with **worry** and **anxiety**—leading to **fear**?

Our emotional responses to **worry**, **anxiety**, and **fear** in times of uncertainty are not new to mankind. Let's look and see how Jesus's disciples responded to times of uncertainty in contrast to how Jesus responded ...

Read Matthew 8:23-27.

"Then Jesus got into the boat and started across the lake with his disciples. Suddenly, a fierce storm struck the lake, with waves breaking into the boat. But Jesus was sleeping. The disciples went and woke him up, shouting, 'Lord, save us! We're going to drown!' Jesus responded, 'Why are you **afraid**? You have so little **faith**!' Then he got up and rebuked the wind and waves, and suddenly there was a great **calm**. The disciples were amazed. "Who is this man?" they asked. "Even the winds and waves obey him'" (NLT)!

 [109]Bob Goff, 50quotesof.com/50-beautiful-sayings-of-bob-goff-that-you-will-love

Now read Matthew 14:22-33.

"After sending them home, he (Jesus) went up into the hills by himself to pray. Night fell while he was there alone. Meanwhile, the disciples were in trouble far away from land, for a strong wind had risen, and they were fighting heavy waves. About three o'clock in the morning Jesus came toward them, walking on the water. When the disciples saw him walking on the water, they were terrified. In their **fear**, they cried out, 'It's a ghost!' But Jesus spoke to them at once. 'Don't be **afraid**,' he said. 'Take courage. I am here! ' Then Peter called to him, 'Lord, if it's really you, tell me to come to you, walking on the water.' 'Yes, come,' Jesus said.

So Peter went over the side of the boat and walked on the water toward Jesus. But when he saw the strong wind and the waves, he was **terrified** and began to sink. 'Save me, Lord.' he shouted. Jesus immediately reached out and grabbed him. 'You have so little **faith**,' Jesus said. 'Why did you doubt me?' When they climbed back into the boat, the wind stopped. Then the disciples worshiped him. 'You really are the Son of God!' they exclaimed" (NLT).

2. In each story, what was the response of the disciples to their circumstances?

3. In Matthew 8, what was Jesus doing during the storm?

4. Why do you think Jesus was able to sleep in the midst of the storm?

5. In Matthew 14, why did Peter begin to sink?

6. Due to the disciples' fearful response, what does Jesus say they are lacking?

In both stories, did you notice that Jesus did not wake up or come immediately? He waited.

7. Why do you think He waited?

God often **tests** our **faith** by **waiting** to answer our cry for help. I have found this biblical concept to be very true in my walk with Christ. It is what you and I do in the waiting time that is important to God: Trust Him or panic?

Both stories followed some of the greatest miracles Jesus ever performed, yet the disciples failed to **trust** the God of miracles.

In Matthew 8, we see the disciples **fretting**, while Jesus was sleeping. They expected Jesus to be as **fearful**, **worrisome**, and **anxious** as they were in the storm. But, Jesus, the Son of God the Creator, knew His father **controlled** the winds and waves. He **rested** in and **trusted** in His father's ability to protect them all. Jesus was at peace in the midst of the storm—as we are to be!

I want to ask you a question. Are you responding to your current "storm" as the disciples did with **worry**, **anxiety**, and **fear** or are you responding as Jesus did with **peace** and **trust** in God Almighty?

8. In the space below, write a prayer of praise thanking God for His control over your life and your circumstances. Thank Him for the gift of **rest** and **peace** and proclaim your **trust** in your Sovereign God.

PONDER:

Worry is nothing but practical infidelity. The person who worries reveals his lack of trust in God and that he is trusting too much in self.[110]
—Lee Roberson

MEDITATE:

Let the peace of Christ rule in your hearts, since as members of one body you were called to peace. And be thankful.
Colossians 3:15

PRAY:

Lord, I am so grateful that when I keep my eyes upon You,
I remain steadfast—never sinking to depths of worry,
anxiety, or fear. You are my Strength, my Refuge, my Strong tower,
my resting place and my source of peace. Help me to allow
Your Spirit full control over my heart, mind, and flesh,
exhibiting the love and peace of Christ in uncertain times.
Amen!

[110]Lee Roberson, https://www.christianquotes.info/quotes-by-topic/quotes-about-worry/

Are you seeking God and His Word to find peace amidst your storm or are you seeking the philosophies of this world? Let's look at ways the world says, according to the Zen: 4 Mindful Practices, we are to deal with uncertainty and stress; contrasting those with what God says.

THE WORLD:

Breathe deeply into the belly. This practice will get you out of your head and into your body. This breathing will calm you and help you to be more present with your body and surroundings.

A friend told me that she was having a large group for dinner. Several days beforehand, her Apple watch began saying, "Breathe, breathe." Apparently due to the anxiety she was feeling, she was unaware that she was holding her breath. Due to the lack of oxygen, she experienced Hypoxic Hypoxia. This means that the low oxygen levels caused histamine to be released into her body and thus the effect on her brain was an increase in wakefulness, reduced appetite, and thirst. So, what does God say?

> *Today many people are arrogant enough to think they don't need God. But, our every breath depends on the life He has breathed into us.[111] NLT Parallel Study Bible*

GOD:

In Ezekiel 37, we see the prophet in a valley filled with dry dead bones. God asked Ezekiel if the bones could come to life again. He replied, "O Sovereign Lord, You alone know the answer to that." Then God tells him to speak these words over the dry bones, "This is what the Sovereign Lord says: 'Look! I am going to put breath into you and make you live again! I will put flesh and muscles on you and cover you with skin. I will put breath into you, and you will come to life. Then you will know that I am the Lord.'" The bones began to rattle and move. They were coming back to life. Ezekiel spoke again, "This is what the Sovereign Lord says: 'Come, O breath, from the four winds! Breathe into these dead bodies so they may live again ... They all came to life and stood up on their feet—a great army'" (NLT).

The dry bones represented those who felt that they were as dead as old dry bones. They felt hopeless. But, God could and would restore them to life. As created beings, God gives us our physical breath. As His children, He puts His life-giving Spirit within us—bringing peace.

No doubt, taking a deep breath can calm a person temporarily. But, breathing will not eliminate our **worry**, **anxiety**, or **fear**. Only the Giver of life and breath, through His Spirit and Word, can breathe calm into our **anxious** hearts.

THE WORLD:

Check on your feelings. Turn your attention to the sensations of your body, notice how uncertainty and fear/anxiety feel for you right now as a bodily experience. Practice giving these feelings some space, letting them be. Then see if you can give them some compassion, to take care of yourself when you're feeling uncertainty.

Showing compassion to your fear and anxiety, is that possible? Compassion is sympathetic consciousness of others' distress together with a desire to alleviate it. According to the definition, we can show compassion towards our fellow man—but not toward our own emotions. We cannot alleviate the **fear** and **anxiety** we feel in times of uncertainty; only God can do that. When we allow **fear** and **anxiety** to just "be," they will consume us! So, what does God say?

 [111]*NLT Parallel Study Bible* (Carol Stream, Illinois: Tyndale House Publishing, 2011). P.1024

GOD:

"The Lord is my light and my salvation, so why should I be afraid? The Lord is my fortress, protecting me from danger, so why should I tremble?" (Psalm 27:1 NLT).

---

*The Lord says, 'I will rescue those who **love** me. I will protect those who **trust** in my name.*
When they call on me, I will answer; I will be with them in trouble.'
Psalm 91:14-15a

---

*Don't be **afraid**, for I am with you. Don't be **discouraged**, for I am your God.*
I will strengthen you and help you. I will hold you up with my victorious right hand.
Isaiah 41:10 NLT

THE WORLD:

Find calm in the middle of a storm. Find your breath. Widen your awareness beyond yourself, and feel the peace of a moment of stillness.

Years ago, while living in Houston, Texas, we endured hurricane Alisha. The front of the storm hit with a fierce intensity. Once the eye of the hurricane was over us there was an eerie sort of calm. We were told not to be fooled by the calm because the back side of the hurricane was going to be more fierce than the front—and it was. We had a false sense of peace in that moment of stillness. In our verses from Matthew, the disciples found calm in the midst of the storm by calling on Jesus and recognizing that He was the only One who could protect them. Being still can bring a temporary sense of calm and peace, but long-lasting true calm and peace can only be found in the Prince of Peace.

GOD:

"The Lord gives strength to his people; the Lord blesses his people with peace" (Psalm 29:11).

So letting your sinful nature control your mind leads to death.
*But letting the Spirit control your mind leads to life and **peace**.*
Romans 8:6 NLT

---

*Now may the Lord of **peace** himself give you his **peace** at all times*
and in every situation. The Lord be with you all.
2 Thessalonians 3:16 NLT

THE WORLD:

Send compassion out to others. Once you have practiced compassion for your own uncertainty and fears—once you have found a moment of calm and centeredness—you can open your heart to others. Feel the fear they are feeling. Send them compassion from the deepest place in your heart. Let it flow out as a healing salve to everyone. Notice how it feels.[112] — zenhabits.com

Yes, we can open our hearts to others showing compassion and exhibiting a spirit of peacefulness and calm, but this can only be accomplished if Christ is living in us. In and of ourselves, our love and compassion for others will diminish, and eventually self will become our main focus. God's Spirit within us gives us the strength and desire to show love and compassion to others. This is what He says:

GOD:

"Each time the Holy Spirit reminds you of scripture, convicts you of sin, restrains you from selfish behavior, or prompts you to love, you have evidence that He is present in you"[113] (NLT Parallel Study Bible).

> *And I will ask the Father, and he will give you another Advocate, who will never leave you. He is the Holy Spirit, who leads into all truth. The world cannot receive him, because it isn't looking for him and doesn't recognize him. But you know him, because he lives with you now and later will be in you.*
> *John 14:16-17 NLT*

The answer to **worry**, **anxiety**, **fear**, and times of uncertainty is not found within one's self. You and I are not an infinite source of **peace**, **rest**, and **safety** amidst the storms of life. But, our trustworthy God is! True **peace**, **rest**, and **safety** can only be found in **Christ** alone!

*In Christ alone my **hope** is found*
*He is my light, my **strength**, my song*
This Cornerstone, this solid ground
Firm through the fiercest drought and storm
*What heights of love, what depths of **peace***
*When **fears** are stilled, when strivings cease*
My Comforter, my All in All
Here in the love of Christ I stand
In Christ alone, who took on flesh
Fullness of God in helpless babe
This gift of love and righteousness
Scorned by the ones He came to save
'Til on that cross as Jesus died
The wrath of God was satisfied
For every sin on Him was laid
Here in the death of Christ I live
There in the ground His body lay
Light of the world by darkness slain

Then bursting forth in glorious Day
Up from the grave He rose again
And as He stands in victory
Sin's curse has lost its grip on me
For I am His and He is mine
Bought with the precious blood of Christ
*No guilt in life, no **fear** in death*
*This is the **power of Christ in me***
From life's first cry to final breath
Jesus commands my destiny
No power of hell, no scheme of man
Can ever pluck me from His hand
Till He returns or calls me home
*Here in the **power of Christ** I'll stand*
I will stand, all other ground is sinking sand
All other ground, all other ground
Is sinking sand, is sinking sand
So I'll stand.[114]

[112]www.zenhabits.com

[113]*NLT Parallel Study Bible* (Carol Stream, Illinois: Tyndale House Publishing, 2011). P.2194

[114]Keith Getty and Stuart Townsend, *In Christ Alone* (Brentwood, Tennessee: EMI Christian Music Publishing, 2001)

Week Eight Menu

Debbie's Stuffed Crust Pizza

¾ cup warm water (100°-110°)

1½ teaspoons sugar

1 package active dry yeast

1¾ cups bread flour

½ teaspoon salt

2 tablespoons canola oil

8 Mozzarella string cheese sticks

Pizza sauce and toppings of choice

1 (8 ounce) Mozzarella, shredded

Garlic salt

Preheat oven to 475°F. Dissolve sugar and yeast in warm water; set aside. In large mixing bowl, mix flour and salt. Make a well in flour and add yeast mixture and oil; mix to form a soft dough. Turn out onto lightly floured surface; knead until the dough is smooth and soft or use bread hook on standing mixer. Lightly oil a second bowl. Place dough in bowl and turn over. Cover and set in a warm place to rise, 1 to 1½ hours, until doubled. Punch dough down; knead on a lightly floured surface for about one minute. Roll into a 16" circle. Place dough on a large baking stone. Place 8 string cheese links around edges. Fold dough around cheese sticks and seal. Spread pizza sauce over crust and place desired topping on sauce. Cover with shredded Mozzarella. Spray edges with cooking spray. Sprinkle with garlic salt. Bake for 15 to 20 minutes or until crust is lightly browned and cheese is bubbly. Note: If white sauce is desired in place of pizza sauce, see recipe below.

Alfredo White Sauce

4 tablespoons unsalted butter

4 tablespoons all-purpose flour

¼ teaspoon salt

Dash of black pepper

1 cup half and half

¾ cup Romano cheese, grated

In saucepan over medium heat, melt butter. Add flour, salt, and pepper. Whisk until well blended. Slowly add half and half and mix well. Cook stirring for two minutes until thickened. Remove from heat; add Romano and mix until melted. Spread onto pizza crust and add toppings.

Salade Parmesan

8 tablespoons Parmesan cheese, grated, divided

¼ cup olive oil

2 tablespoons fresh lemon juice

1 tablespoon dry mustard

½ teaspoon cracked pepper

2 cloves garlic, mined

Dash of salt

10 to 12 cups Romaine lettuce, torn

In a large bowl, combine 6 tablespoons Parmesan cheese, olive oil, lemon juice, dry mustard, pepper, garlic, and salt. Mix well. Pour over salad greens. Toss well. Sprinkle with remaining Parmesan cheese. Top with homemade croutons. Serve immediately.

Homemade Buttery Croutons

½ loaf French bread, cut into cubes

¼ teaspoon garlic powder (more or less depending on your taste)

½ cup butter, melted

Preheat oven to 375°F. Place bread cubes into large bowl. In separate small bowl, stir garlic powder into melted butter and very slowly drizzle over bread cubes. Use a large spoon to lightly stir the cubes from the bottom of the bowl to allow the garlic butter to coat them evenly. Spread on cookie sheet. Bake for 10 to 15 minutes, stirring occasionally until lightly golden brown. Note: You may use any kind of left over or stale bread.

Build Your Own Sundae

Variety of ice cream

Fruit, sliced strawberries, bananas, blueberries

Maraschino cherries

Fudge, chocolate, or caramel sauce

Fresh whipped cream

Chopped nuts, any variety

You will need big bowls to have room for the goodies above!

Hot Fudge Sauce

⅔ cup heavy cream

½ cup light corn syrup

⅓ cup dark brown sugar

¼ cup cocoa powder

¼ teaspoon sea salt

6 ounce bittersweet chocolate, chopped, divided in half

2 tablespoons unsalted butter

1 teaspoon vanilla extract

In a 2-quart saucepan over medium-high heat, bring the cream, corn syrup, brown sugar, cocoa powder, salt, and half the chocolate to a slow boil. Reduce heat to low maintaining a low simmer, and cook for 5 minutes, stirring occasionally. Remove from the heat and stir in the remaining chocolate, butter, and vanilla extract, stirring until smooth. Let cool for 20 to 30 minutes before using (thickens as it cools). Store in airtight jar or container in the refrigerator for up to 2 weeks.

Salted Caramel Sauce

1½ cups sugar

½ cup water

1 teaspoon sea salt

1 cup heavy cream

1 teaspoon vanilla extract

Place sugar in a medium heavy-bottomed saucepan and stir in ½ cup water. Place over medium-high heat and cook, without stirring, for 15 to 16 minutes, until dark amber color. Remove from heat and stir in salt. Gradually stir in heavy cream and vanilla. Cool and spoon into jar. Tightly seal and store in refrigerator for up to 2 weeks. <u>Note</u>: Do not use nonstick pan as it will cause caramel to crystalize.

SHORT-CUTS...

- **DEBBIE'S STUFFED CRUST PIZZA:** Process can be hastened by using *Rapid-Rise* yeast.

- **DEBBIE'S STUFFED CRUST PIZZA:** When not stuffing the crust with cheese sticks, you can prepare pizza dough days ahead, place on baking sheet, cover with plastic wrap and freeze.

- **DEBBIE'S STUFFED CRUST PIZZA:** Cut all vegetables for the pizza and salad the night before, or morning of your meal, store in air-tight containers in refrigerator.

- **SALADE PARMESAN:** Make this mock Caesar salad ahead of time by mixing the dressing in the bowl and laying the lettuce on top, unmixed until serving time, refrigerate.

- **SALADE PARMESAN:** Make croutons up to a week ahead and store in airtight container.

- **BUILD YOUR OWN SUNDAE:** Make the sauces for ice cream up to two weeks ahead and store in airtight containers in refrigerator. Wash and cut berries the night before or the morning of, and store in air-tight container in refrigerator. Make homemade ice cream a day ahead and freeze.

HEALTHY TIPS...

- **DEBBIE'S STUFFED CRUST PIZZA:** Make your own crust using a whole wheat or Gluten-free crust recipe; easily found on Pinterest.

- **DEBBIE'S STUFFED CRUST PIZZA:** Use unbleached flour.

- **DEBBIE'S STUFFED CRUST PIZZA:** Purchase nitrate-free Canadian bacon, pepperoni, or healthy meat of your choice.

- **DEBBIE'S STUFFED CRUST PIZZA:** Use olive oil in place of canola oil in recipe. Brush edges of crust with olive oil instead of using non-stick spray.

- **DEBBIE'S STUFFED CRUST PIZZA:** If you are concerned about fat and calories, cut the cheese amount in half.

- **SALADE PARMESAN:** Make your own croutons with whole wheat, whole grain bread, or gluten-free bread. Recipe included.

- **BUILD YOUR OWN SUNDAE:** Make your own homemade ice cream with fresh products.

- **BUILD YOUR OWN SUNDAE:** When reading nutritional labels on ice cream cartons, you will find that most have additives and contain very few dairy products. Some containers lurking in the freezer section of your local grocery aren't even Ice Cream; if you look closely they will be labeled as Frozen Dessert. What you thought was Ice Cream is not Ice Cream at all!

- **BUILD YOUR OWN SUNDAE:** Make your own homemade caramel or fudge sauce. They will still contain sugar, but not the preservatives and large amounts of fructose corn syrup found in store-bought brands. <u>Note</u>: The fudge recipe in this section includes corn syrup; the caramel sauce does not.

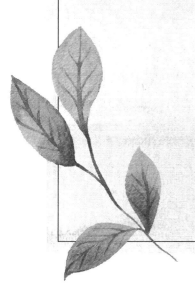

Hurts

A stiff apology is a second insult.
The injured party does not want to be compensated because he has been wronged; he wants to be healed because he has been hurt.

—G.K. Chesterton

*P*ainful wounds, both physical and emotional, can go deeper than the surface of the skin. Physical wounds can vary in their severity depending on the depth of the lesion. In contrast, emotional wounds or hurts go deep into the heart of every person whom they have been inflicted upon.

I was reading about treatments for physical wounds, and it said that the type of treatment would depend on several things: the type of wound, the cause of the wound, and the depth of the wound. Take, for instance, minor wounds. These typically heal on their own and require little to no treatment. The more serious the wound, the more intense the treatment. But, in the case of all physical wounds, it is necessary to care for them until they heal completely, to avoid a serious infection.

Emotional wounds, on the other hand, must be treated differently than physical wounds. Just like physical wounds, the treatment will depend upon the type of wound, the cause of the wound, and the depth of the wound. Many people, myself included, grew up in an emotionally or physically abusive environment where a parent, teacher, or an authority figure regularly degraded, and belittled them, or took advantage of them physically. Others may be involved in an emotionally abusive marriage or living arrangement. Both types of abuse can cause deep wounds.

In God's Word we learn of a Man who suffered both physical and emotional wounds. He took his wounds to the only One who could heal and use them for the good of all mankind.

In Matthew, we see how people inflicted physical and emotional wounds upon Him, "Then they began to spit in Jesus' face and beat him with their fists and some slapped him, jeering, 'Prophesy to us, you Messiah! Who hit you that time?' ... "Some of the governor's soldiers took Jesus into their headquarters. They stripped him and put a scarlet robe on him. They wove thorn branches into a crown and put it on his head. Then they knelt before him in mockery and taunted, 'Hail! King of the Jews!' And they spit on him and struck him on the head. Then they led him away to be crucified ..."

"The people passing by shouted abuse, shaking their heads in mockery. 'Look at you now!' they yelled at him. "You said you were going to destroy the Temple and rebuild it in three days. Well then, if you are the Son of God, save yourself and come down from the cross!" At about three o'clock, Jesus called out with a loud voice, 'My God, my God, why have you abandoned me? Then Jesus shouted out again, and he released his spirit'" (Matthew 26:67-68, 27:27-31, 39-41, 46, 50 NLT).

Jesus **willingly** endured physical and emotional wounds for us. I don't know about you, but I have never **willingly** endured physical or emotional wounds! But because they are a part of life, we have no choice. When we are wounded, scarring can occur. Jesus bore the scars of His wounding, and they told the story. If we allow God, He will use the scarring from our emotional wounds to tell a story that will encourage others, heal our hearts, and bring glory to Him.

Our infirmities become the black velvet on which the diamond of God's love glitters all the more brightly.[115] *— Charles Spurgeon*

Day One

This week we are going to draw a parallel between five different types of open wounds and the emotional wounds that we often experience in life. We will look into God's Word to find the treatment for these wounds and the ways in which we can allow Him to utilize the scars that remain.

Today, we will be talking about an **Abrasion** wound; contrasting the physical and emotional.

An **Abrasion** occurs when the skin rubs or scrapes against a rough or hard surface. There is usually not much bleeding, but the wound needs to be scrubbed and cleaned well to avoid infection.

1. Fill in the missing words from the following verse: "The _____ of the godly are a _____-_____ fountain; the _____ of the wicked conceal violent intentions" (Proverbs 10:11 NLT).

Words are powerful! They can bring life to a person or death. Life, in that they can encourage and lift up a person or death in that they can kill a person's spirit and destroy their self-worth. Unkind or harsh words spoken to us can scrape and rub our spirit. They can be hurtful and leave an abrasion-**type** wound in our hearts and souls.

2. Have the words of another person spoken to you brought an **abrasion-type** wound to your heart and spirit? Explain.

When we love, we open ourselves to the possibility of hurt.[116]
—Linda Dillow

In loving others, we are taking a chance that we will be hurt. Those we love can hurt us, but we can also hurt those we love. We can be the one inflicting an abrasion-type wound on those close to us.

[116]Linda Dillow, *Calm My Anxious Heart* (Colorado Springs, Colorado: Nav Press, 2007). P. 75

3. Now, let's consider a time when your words brought an **abrasion-type** wound to someone else's heart and spirit. Tell of such a time.

Typically, at the core of our hurtful and harsh words, there is a **heart** issue. Basically, at the root of every sin issue in the life of a believer is a spiritual problem—a **heart** issue. Read the verse below.

> *Test me, Lord, and try me, examine my heart and my mind ...*
> *Psalm 26:2 NIV*

4. Using the verse above, ask God to examine your **heart** related to the hurtful words you spoke in the story written in Question #3. Ask Him to forgive you and change your **heart** that your words might be honoring to you, Him, and others.

5. Ask God to reveal to you what was in your **heart** that lead to such harsh and painful words? Was it jealousy and envy? Was it a result of spiritual coldness in your heart and life? What did He reveal?

When a member of my family called me and wanted to meet, I said that would be fine and asked when and where. She told me that she would come to my house. When she arrived, she had another family member with her. As she began the conversation, it was obvious she had many issues with me. I was unaware of many of them. Her words stung like large raindrops pelting against your skin during a summer storm.

I felt as if I had a target on my chest, and all the flaming darts were aimed at the black dot in the middle, positioned over my heart. Her words were intense and painful; her anger seemed to have no end. With her words she wounded me. After two hours of sitting and listening to her with little response from me, I was thankful when they left.

As I lay in bed that night, floods of tears began to fall down my cheeks. The pain of the wound was so intense that my heart felt as though it would leap from my chest. I began to pray, asking God to show me if there was any truth in what she had said. I was willing to acknowledge my wrongdoing. God revealed that there was some truth to what she had said that night. He also revealed that her arrows were launched from a hurting heart.

I could not sleep. So, I got up and wrote a letter to her and the other family member. It is still in my computer because once I came to understand that she was in a place of pain and hurt, confusion, and disappointment in God, I could **forgive** her. She was struggling to understand what God was allowing to take place in our lives at the time. Her verbal attack on me was really her striking out at God. No need to send the letter!

I was able to forgive them both, and, through the power of **forgiveness**, the **abrasion** was healed.

Bear with each other and forgive one another if any of you has a
grievance against someone. Forgive as the Lord forgave you.
Colossians 3:13 NIV

In order for healing to take place, cleansing must occur
and cleansing begins with forgiveness.

If we live long enough and love long enough we will be wounded, and we will inflict wounds upon others. Just ask any woman if she has been hurt by the words of someone she cared deeply about in the past few months and would surely say, "Yes." Because of our fleshly nature, our words can intentionally or unintentionally hurt someone we care about deeply. We are all going to experience an **abrasion** wound of some kind through the words and actions of others and we are all going to inflict an **abrasion** wound at some point.

6. According to Colossians 3:13, how are we to treat the emotional **abrasion** wound inflicted upon us by the words of others?

7. According to Proverbs 13:3, how do we keep from inflicting **abrasion** wounds upon others through our words?

When our **heart** is guarded, our words will be guarded!

The treatment for verbal **abrasions** begins with first guarding our **heart**. Let's look at the verse we reflected upon earlier in our study. Perhaps, we need to be reminded of it when considering our words.

> *Above all else, guard your **heart**, for everything you do*
> *(even your words) flows from it.*
> *Proverbs 4:23 NIV*

PONDER:

Be careful with your words. Once they are said, they can only be forgiven not forgotten.
—Author Unknown

MEDITATE:

If you forgive those who sin against you, your Heavenly Father will forgive you.
But if you refuse to forgive others, your Father will not forgive your sins.
Matthew 6:14-15 NLT

PRAY:

Dear God, there is no doubt that at some point in life, I am going to be
hurt by the words of others and I am going to inflict hurt on others through
he words I speak. If I hurt others with my words, grant me the strength
to apologize. If people hurt me with their words, grant me the strength
to forgive. Father, You have forgiven me much, may I forgive much.
Amen!

Day Two

It was a beautiful day and I wanted to get out of the house for a while, so I drove to my daughter's home. We were all on lock down due to COVID-19. My youngest granddaughter, Ainsley, had experienced a bike accident the day before and as we were sitting in the garage talking about her injuries, we began sharing each of our childhood stories of cuts, bruises, and broken bones.

We were rolling up our sleeves and pantlegs to show everyone our **scars** and share our stories of how each happened. It seemed that the deeper the wound the more prevalent the **scar**. As we were sharing, it dawned on me that all **scars** tell a story.

Scars not only tell a story, but they give evidence or proof of the **incision wound** inflicted. We see this in the book of John. Jesus's **scars** told the story of what had happened just days prior to His seeing His disciples once again.

1. Fill in the blanks of the following verse: "That Sunday evening the disciples were meeting behind locked doors because they were afraid of the Jewish leaders. Suddenly, Jesus was standing there among them! "_____ be with you," he said. As he spoke, he _____ them the _____ in his hands and his side. They were filled with joy when they saw the Lord!" (John 20:20 NLT).

The **incision scars** in His hands, feet, and side gave proof of not only the **wounds** inflicted upon Him, but of His identity. Those **scars** distinguished Him from the rest of mankind.

2. Write the definition of an **incision** wound.

Incisions can be painful and have long-lasting complications. Those inflicted upon us by others, whether from being falsely accused of wrongdoing or having ugly and deceptive things said about us, can cause emotional bleeding. If not treated correctly, and time allowed for complete healing, they can leave deep **scars**.

Years ago, we were headed for Florida for a family vacation. We had looked forward to the time on the beach, relaxing and forgetting about work and home. As Mark wrapped up work at his office, I packed the car. We met and picked up the girls from their last day of school. After three hours, we stopped for dinner. As we returned to the car, our older daughter, Angela, began to complain about her stomach hurting. Thinking it was the greasy fast food we had just eaten, we suggested she sleep and then see how she was feeling. Her symptoms seemed to subside as the night wore on.

We arrived late into the night, unloaded, and headed to bed. When we awoke the next morning, Angela was in pain once again. So, since we have a doctor in the family, we called him. We described her symptoms. He listed several possibilities and suggested that we keep an eye on her. She made it through the week without any further intense pain, and by the time our vacation was over, she seemed back to normal.

After being home just three days, the abdominal issues flared up again. We called our doctor, and he suggested we come in the following morning. By the next afternoon, Angela was in surgery for appendicitis. They removed her appendix, which was inflamed and enlarged. The **incision** was deep. Upon her release, we were given instructions on how to care for the **incision**, so that it would heal properly. We did exactly what we were told, but after four days, she was having a great deal of pain. The surgeon asked us to come to the office. What he discovered was an infection in the **incision**. He had to reopen it in order to clean and treat it properly. In order for the **incision** to heal properly, he could not close it completely. We were given a new set of instructions for treatment.

3. How should you treat an **incision** wound inflicted upon you from being falsely accused of wrongdoing, having ugly and deceptive things said about you, or being physically mistreated?

> *Forgiveness is not something that you say with your mouth.*
> *It is something that you do with your **heart**.*[117]
> —*Fritz Chery*

"And Jesus said, Father, forgive them, for they know not what they do" (Luke 23:34 ESV). These are Jesus's words to His heavenly Father as to those who had inflicted incision wounds upon Him.

Many spit on Jesus, stripped Him, pierced His side with a sword, yelled disgraceful things at Him, and drove spikes into His hands and feet. They pinned Him to a cross to die, yet He interceded for them, asking God to **forgive** them. What an example Christ set for us!

Again, in order for **healing** to take place, cleansing must occur, and cleansing occurs through **forgiveness**. Healing of emotional **incisions** will take place when **forgiveness** is given!

An open **incision** needs a great deal of cleaning to **heal** properly. When the **incision** is deep, the tendons, ligaments, and muscles risk being damaged. Apparently Angela's was deep. Years later, with each pregnancy, she experienced pain as her babies grew, pushing on the muscles that had been cut as a result of the appendectomy **incision** and the **scarring** that had occurred in the healing process.

4. Write the definition of the word **scar**.

Our **scars** are specific to us and so is the **story** that goes along with each one. I don't know of anyone who has a **scar** on their left forearm along their main artery from a broken Ball jar while playing in the

[117]Fritz Chery, www.biblereasons.com/Article: January 8, 2020

basement of a family friend—but I do. I don't remember the day my parents rushed me to the hospital bleeding profusely, but they have told me the **story** numerous times. When an **incision** is inflicted whether by the words or actions of others, or by a cut, **scarring** can often occur.

God turns emotional **scars** into **stories**. My friend, Angel, was **scarred** by a rape. My brother, Paul, was **scarred** by the harsh critical words of my dad. My friend, Ashley was **scarred** by betrayal. My friend, Jenny, was **scarred** by the alcoholism and divorce of her parents. If we **allow** God, He will use the **scarring** from our emotional **incision** wounds to tell a **story** that will encourage others, heal our hearts, and bring glory to Him.

5.   Write Romans 8:28.

6.   Romans 8:28 contains a promise. What is God's promise found in this verse?

No matter the **incision**, if we allow God to treat the wound with His healing balm, He will use whatever wound we have experienced in this life for our good and His glory!

PONDER:

Forgive others as quickly as you expect God to forgive you.
—Author Unknown

MEDITATE:

For I will forgive their wickedness and will remember their sins no more.
Hebrews 8:12 NIV

PRAY:

God, Your Son showed abundant mercy and grace toward those who
had inflicted incision wounds upon Him. Help me to faithfully follow His
example in forgiving others who inflict incision wounds upon me. Tell my story
with the scars I have experienced and use them for my good, for the good of
those around me, and for Your glory.
Amen!

Day Three

A **laceration** is an irregular or jagged break or tearing of the skin. It is often caused from accidents with tools or machinery and bleeds rapidly and extensively.

As we sat in Angela's garage sharing our **scar** stories, I told my grandchildren about a **scar** I have on my back and how I got it.

It was a warm spring day in Lawrence, Kansas. Storms were predicted for that night. Our bedroom window was open and the winds were tossing the curtains back and forth. We didn't take the time to close it before heading to church. While we were gone, the winds began to increase and the storm clouds rolled in on thunderous claps of lightning.

Once home, typical of children, my sister and I didn't notice the wet nightstand in our bedroom and the things strewn on the floor beside the bed. As we entered the room, she pushed me, I pushed back, and we ended up wrestling on the bed. After one hard shove, I rolled off the side of the bed near the edge of the nightstand. As I landed, I felt something sharp and sleek enter my back. The pain was piercing. Blood began to flow, and my sister yelled for my parents. It bled a lot and for several minutes.

What we had not bothered to notice was the drinking glass that had blown off the nightstand and onto the floor. There were shards of glass everywhere. The base of the glass was still intact with a sharply jagged piece attached. That is what entered my back as I landed on the floor. I had a rather large **laceration** as a result of that fall. It was so deep that for months I was unable to do cartwheels or any other physical activity that required raising my arms above my head. Eventually it healed, but I have an obvious **scar** that will never go away.

Laceration wounds are much deeper than an **abrasion** or an **incision** wound. In life, we can experience a **laceration** wound, an irregular or jagged break or tear in our emotional being that can result in painful **scarring**. These wounds can often be inflicted upon us by our own choices and actions.

Over my years of being in full-time vocational ministry, I have witnessed young women make unwise and selfish choices in an effort to be happy because they "deserved" happiness. But, many times the result has been anything but happiness. The **laceration** wound they inflicted upon themselves in an effort to be happy caused great tragedy and sadness in their lives and in the lives of those who loved them.

1. Write Proverbs 12:15 below.

2. Tell of a time when your own actions brought about an emotional **laceration** wound?

One of the tragedies of self-inflicted **lacerations** resulting from our own choices and actions is Satan's lie that we can never be **forgiven**. This is not true! God not only **forgives**, but He **heals** and **restores**— He binds up our wounds.

3. Fill in the blanks of the following verse: "But you, O Lord, are a _____ and _____God. You are patient, always _____ and ready to _____" (Psalm 86:15 GW).

Another tragedy I see is young women who are unable to **forgive** themselves, even after God has **forgiven** them. Satan lies and tells them that the wrong choices they made should be paid for the rest of their lives—inflicting relentless judgment upon themselves!

Their **laceration** wound remains open and oozing with the lies of Satan. He tells them that their choices are too severe and too awful for God to **forgive**, thus they should carry the burden of shame and are undeserving of anyone's **forgiveness**.

When we return to God, broken and bleeding, He promises to **forgive**, **heal**, and **restore** us completely. He sets us free from the pain of our wounds.

4. Read the following verse aloud. Claim it and believe it.

> *There is therefore now **no condemnation** for those who are in Christ Jesus. For the law of the Spirit of life has set you free in Christ Jesus from the law of sin and death.*
> *Romans 8:1-2 ESV*

5. If you are living in the dark pain and lie of **unforgiveness** for past choices that caused emotional **laceration** wounds, pray and ask God to **forgive** you, then accept His **forgiveness**. Write your prayer below.

6. If you are living in the dark pain of past choices that caused emotional **laceration** wounds and have not **allowed yourself grace and forgiveness**, pray and ask God to help you to **forgive** yourself. Thank Him and embrace the new person God is creating in you. Write your prayer below.

As Christians, we are **new creatures**, in Christ Jesus. This means that our old man was atoned for by His blood through his sacrificial death on the cross. We receive eternal life through Jesus Christ. He came to die so that we might live as new creatures in Him.

Spend time today reading Matthew chapters 26-28. This is a lot of reading, but in sacrificing the time, you will be reminded of the intense **laceration wounds** inflicted upon Christ, so that we might receive **complete healing** for ours!

Meditate on the quote below. What a powerful truth. It was because of Christ's death that we live **healed** of the pain of life's choices, **forgiven**, and **restored** to new life.

PONDER:

On the peak of Calvary's hill, we find strength for our weakness,
grace for our sin, and life for our death.[118]
—Jon Weece

MEDITATE:

For Christ also suffered once for sins, the righteous for the unrighteous, that he might
bring us to God, being put to death in the flesh but made alive in the spirit ...
1 Peter 3:8 ESV

PRAY:

Father, laceration wounds are deep and painful. They are often self-inflicted
due to the presence of sin in my life, or as a result of wrongful decisions.
I am grateful for Your Son's sacrificial death that provided forgiveness for my sins.
I am thankful that not only do You forgive me, but You provide the strength
needed for me to forgive myself. You have set me free of Satan's lies.
You are creating a new beautiful woman who is unchained from her past.
Amen!

[118]Jon Weece, Jesus Prom, (Nashville, Tennessee: Thomas Nelson, 2014). P. 154

Day Four

As with laceration wounds, a **puncture** wound can sometimes be inflicted upon us by our own actions or through the wrongful or unfair actions of others.

One interesting fact about a **puncture** wound is that although it may not bleed much, it can go deep enough to damage internal organs—such as the heart!

Let's take a look at a man in God's Word who was falsely accused and how he responded to the wounds inflicted upon him.

Read Acts 6:8-15 and Acts 7:1-60

1. How was Stephen described in Acts 6:8?

2. What was Stephen doing at the time he was falsely accused?

3. What did the false witnesses accuse him of doing (Acts 6:1-14)?

4. What was Stephen's punishment?

These men lied about Stephen, causing him to be arrested and
brought before the Jewish high council.[119]
NLT Parallel Study Bible

---

  [119]*NLT Parallel Study Bible* (Carol Stream, Illinois: Tyndale House Publishing, 2011). P. 2051

We may feel that Stephen had the right to be angry with the witnesses who falsely accused him of wrong doing. Although he may have had the right, he showed no anger towards his accusers, only love and forgiveness. He lived up to the description Luke gave of him, "a man full of God's grace."

5. Fill the following blanks of Proverbs 6:16-19:"There are six things that the Lord hates, seven that are an abomination to him: haughty eyes, _____ _____ _____, and hands that shed _____ blood, a _____ that devises _____ plans, feet that make haste to _____ to evil, a false witness who breathes out lies, and one who sows discord among brothers" (ESV).

God never condones the mistreatment of our fellow human beings. According to the verse above, He hates, "a **lying** tongue, hands that **shed innocent** blood, a heart that **devises wicked** schemes, feet that are quick to **rush** into **evil**, a **false** witness who pours out **lies** and a person who **stirs up** conflict in the community."

I was looking through the books that once belonged to my husband, Mark, and came upon the autobiography of a Bulgarian pastor named Haralan Povoc. His story is not only one of intense deep emotional and physical wounding inflicted upon him, but of God's ability to weave a tapestry of forgiveness into the human heart.

- Haralan was born on a farm in Krasno Gradiste, Bulgaria. He was one of four children and his family was very poor. The small farmhouse where he and his family lived had dirt floors and all four children slept in one room. Haralan worked from a young age for other, larger farms in the area. He did not have a pair of *proper* shoes until the age of 17. He says of himself, "I grew up rather egotistical, and as an atheist. That's a bad combination!"[120]

- In November of 1925, while still a young man, he moved in with a friend named Christo. It was this friend who invited him to church. He reluctantly went, and heard about God for the first time. He had never experienced worship or seen a Bible until he began going to church with Christo. He said of the experience, "For the first time, I heard educated and cultured people openly testifying that God exists! They told what Christ meant to them and had done for them. This impressed me more than all the sermons, and to this day, I am a strong believer in the effectiveness of "living testimonies" in bringing men to Christ."[121]

A man in the church named Petroff became his discipling teacher, and, feeling called to preach, Haralan later left Bulgaria for England to attend Danzig Bible Institute. There he met the young woman who would become his wife. Ruth was originally from Sweden. They married and returned to Bulgaria where he pastored a church for sixteen years before WWII began.

- He says of those days, "In 1944 a dark menace came riding into our homeland on the heels of the Russian army: the menace of communism. In three years, the other parties were banned, their leaders imprisoned and the Communist party was in full control."[122]

- "At 4 a.m. on July 24, 1948, my doorbell suddenly started ringing insistently over and over. Sleepily I arose, put my robe on and went to the door. There stood three strangers, two of whom in ordinary clothes and the other in a uniform. 'We have come to search your house.'

[120]Haralan Povoc, *Tortured for His Faith* (Grand Rapids, Michigan: Zondervan Publishing House, 1978). P. 16
[121]Haralan Povoc, *Tortured for His Faith* (Grand Rapids, Michigan: Zondervan Publishing House, 1978). P. 17
[122]Haralan Povoc, *Tortured for His Faith* (Grand Rapids, Michigan: Zondervan Publishing House, 1978). P. 19

They searched everywhere—through books, beds, bookshelves, storage chests, drawers—for three hours. They didn't miss anything! They turned to me and ordered me to come along with them and said I must come long but it was only for ' a little questioning,' they explained. Little did I know that this "little questioning" would last for thirteen endless years of torture and imprisonment."[123]

As I read of the intense torture and punishment Haralan Povoc endured for his faith, I found myself crying. He was beaten almost to death numerous times, forced to stand for days and answer questions, and if the questions were not answered in the manner the Communist wanted, he was hit forcefully in the face. He was placed in deep dark holes within prisons, slept on mud floors, dressed in rags, spent nine months in solitary confinement, ravaged by bed bugs and other insects, forced to work in freezing temperatures without any outer wear for protection, and starved and left for dead.

- He said of those who tortured him, "Step by step, as they brutalized prisoners and beat us, they descended down a ladder of humanity to the level of beasts. Their faces, after time, defied description and they became like animals. We prisoners would eventually recover, but the guards suffered a permanent crippling of their humanity."[124]

Both Haralan and Stephen were persecuted for their faith in God. Each saw that the wounds inflicted upon them were the result of wickedness within the hearts of men. They knew God would redeem their pain and suffering and that those responsible would in the end pay a great price!

These were Stephen's words of forgiveness, "Lord, do not hold this sin against them." When he had said this, he died. Stephen followed Christ's example for these were His words on the cross.

Jesus, Stephen, and Haralan Povoc, had horrific **puncture wounds** inflicted upon them by wicked and lost men. Yet, each one forgave those who had wounded them. Can you not find it in your heart to do the same?

6. Are you withholding forgiveness from someone who has wounded you? Why?

Haralan wrote in the introduction of his book, "My purpose in this book is not to show man's depravity; the depravity tells its own story and I experienced it night and day for more than thirteen years. No, my purpose is to show God's overwhelming love. If anything should stand out in this book, let it be the overwhelming truth of God's love in the midst of man's bestiality."[125]

God's Love = Forgiveness!

[123]Haralan Povoc, *Tortured for His Faith* (Grand Rapids, Michigan: Zondervan Publishing House, 1978). P. 9
[124]Haralan Povoc, *Tortured for His Faith* (Grand Rapids, Michigan: Zondervan Publishing House, 1978). P. 28
[125]Haralan Povoc, *Tortured for His Faith* (Grand Rapids, Michigan: Zondervan Publishing House, 1978). P. 1

PONDER:

Holding a grudge doesn't make you strong, it makes you bitter,
forgiving doesn't make you weak, it sets you free.
—Author Unknown

MEDITATE:

But to you who are listening I say: Love your enemies, do good
to those who hate you, bless those who curse you, pray for those
who mistreat you. If someone slaps you on one cheek, turn to them the
other also. If someone takes your coat, do not withhold your shirt from them.
Give to everyone who asks you, and if anyone takes what belongs to you,
do not demand it back. Do to others as you would have them do to you.
But love your enemies, do good to them, and lend to them without expecting
to get anything back. Then your reward will be great, and you will be children
of the Most High, because he is kind to the ungrateful and wicked.
Be merciful, just as your Father is merciful.
Matthew 6:27-31, 35-36 NIV

PRAY:

Lord God, I know nothing of the suffering endured by your Son,
the disciple, Stephen, or Pastor Povoc. In reading their stories, I stand amazed
at their love for those who hurt them, and the forgiveness freely given to those who
so deeply wounded them. Father, help me, like these, to be more concerned about the
hearts of those who inflict wounds than the damage done. May the scars of my
wounds tell the story of love, mercy, forgiveness, and restoration for me and for
those who caused them.
Amen!

Day Five

An **avulsion** is a partial or complete tearing away of skin and tissue. **Avulsions** usually occur during violent accidents, such as body-crushing accidents, explosions, and gunshots. They bleed heavily and rapidly. An emotional **avulsion** can tear your heart from your chest. It is painful and often causes heavy bleeding.

On April 19, 1995, the deadliest domestic terrorist incident in United States history occurred:

> "The Oklahoma City bombing was a domestic terrorist truck bombing on the Alfred P. Murrah Federal Building in Oklahoma City, Oklahoma, United States on April 19, 1995. Perpetrated by Timothy McVeigh and Terry Nichols, the bombing happened at 9:02 am and killed at least 168 people, injured more than 680 others, and destroyed one-third of the building. The blast destroyed or damaged 324 other buildings within a 16-block radius, shattered glass in 258 nearby buildings, and destroyed or burned 86 cars, causing an estimated $652 million worth of damage. Local, state, federal, and worldwide agencies engaged in extensive rescue efforts in the wake of the bombing, and substantial donations were received from across the country. The Federal Emergency Management Agency (FEMA) activated 11 of its Urban Search and Rescue Task Forces, consisting of 665 rescue workers who assisted in rescue and recovery operations. Until the September 11, 2001 attacks, the Oklahoma City bombing was the deadliest terrorist attack in the history of the United States, and remains the deadliest incident of domestic terrorism in the country's history."[126]

If you research this historical event you will discover the *motive* given for the attack: "Motivated by his dislike for the U.S. federal government and unhappy about its handling of the Ruby Ridge incident in 1992 and the Waco siege in 1993, McVeigh timed his attack to coincide with the second anniversary of the deadly fire that ended the siege at the Branch Davidian compound in Waco, Texas."[127]

The motive listed in the federal report was *anti-government sentiment*. In other words **hatred**.

- Why did the Pharisees want Jesus crucified? **Hatred**.

- Why did the people stone Stephen? **Hatred**.

- Why did the Communist imprison, beat, torture, and curse Haralan Povoc? **Hatred**.

Hatred may seem like a "harsh" word to use, but **hatred** it was. In order for you to understand why I used this word, let's look at what it means.

1. Write the definition of the word **hatred** below.

[126]en.wickepedia.com/Oklahoma City Bombing
[127]en.wickepedia.com/Oklahoma City Bombing

It is the extreme dislike, resentment, and ill-will in the hearts of people that causes them to wound others—both physically and emotionally.

2. Write two or three antonyms for the word **hatred**.

3. What is the meaning of an **antonym**? What do you notice about the definition of **hatred** versus the **antonyms** given for this word?

Affection, fondness, devotion, and **love**—these are the exact opposite of the word **hatred**.

God says in Luke 6:27-30, "Bless those who curse you, pray for those who mistreat you. If someone slaps you on one cheek, turn to them the other also. If someone takes your coat, do not withhold your shirt from them. Give to everyone who asks you, and if anyone takes what belongs to you, do not demand it back" (NIV).

God asks us, as His children, to respond in a way that is opposite of the world's response. When we are wounded and hurt, we are to love and forgive. Jesus did! Stephen did! Haralan Povoc did!

> *I don't label myself as a hero or martyr, but as I neared my release*
> *and looked back I could honestly and truthfully say that it was worth*
> *those 13 years of torture, beatings, starvation, suffering, and separation*
> *from loved ones to be a "pastor" to the thousands of communist*
> *prisoners my path had crossed.[128]*
> *—Haralon Povoc*

In being freed he said, "As I stood looking at the prison walls behind me, I thought, 'Yes, to leave behind men who know and serve Christ, it is worth it all.' And it truly was. I can honestly say before God it was worth it all."[129] —Haralan Povoc

Now that is **forgiveness**!

---

[128]Haralan Povoc, *Tortured for His Faith* (Grand Rapids, Michigan: Zondervan Publishing House, 1978). P. 112
[129]Haralan Povoc, *Tortured for His Faith* (Grand Rapids, Michigan: Zondervan Publishing House, 1978). P. 114

Jesus, Stephen, and Pastor Povoc **forgave** those who had wounded them so deeply. Their wounds were redeemed for the good of mankind. At the cost of their suffering and sacrifice, many in this world have come to know God.

In the months following the bombing in Oklahoma City, many loved ones placed signs at the location of the bombing. There was one such sign placed on the end of a fence by a father who had lost his little boy. Paper clipped to the corner of the poster board was a picture of his son. With black marker he had placed a rough drawing of a cross and under the cross he had written these words: "Because of the cross I can forgive Timothy McVeigh. Because of heaven, I will see my son again one day."[130]

Now that is **forgiveness! Forgiveness** for one of the deepest **avulsion** wounding's any one could experience in life—the senseless and brutal murder of a child. In this life, we will be **wounded** and we will inflict **wounds** upon others.

WHEN WOUNDED:

- We must acknowledge our wounds.

- We must allow God to heal our wounds.

- We must forgive those who inflicted the wounds.

- We must allow God to redeem our scars for our good, the good of those around us, and for His glory.

WHEN WE WOUND OTHERS:

- We should search our heart for the motive behind our wounding and confess it.

- We must acknowledge our sin.

- We should ask God and the one whom we have wounded to forgive us.

- We should allow God to use the situation to give us a better understanding of His forgiveness in our lives.

It is said of Haralan Povoc, "A man of God disappeared into Communist prisons—thirteen years later a spiritual giant came out."[131]

God desires to use the wounds that occur in our lives to stretch our faith, deepen our level of compassion, and weave a tapestry of unconditional love and forgiveness in our hearts for others.

[130]en.wickepedia.com/Oklahoma City Bombing
[131]Haralan Povoc, *Tortured for His Faith* (Grand Rapids, Michigan: Zondervan Publishing House, 1978). Cover

PONDER:

Life becomes easier when you learn to accept an apology you never got.
—Author Unknown

MEDITATE:

Therefore, as God's chosen people, holy and dearly loved, clothe yourselves with compassion, kindness, humility, gentleness and patience. Bear with each other and forgive one another if any of you has a grievance against someone. Forgive as the Lord forgave you. And over all these virtues put on love, which binds them all together in perfect unity.
Matthew 6:27-31, 35-36 NIV

PRAY:

Father God, do not allow the wounds inflicted upon me to be a distraction, drawing me away for You. When I am wounded, help me to love and quickly forgive the one inflicting the wound. When I wound those I love, show me the motive behind the wounding. Cleanse me of the sin of jealousy, envy, hatred, and wickedness. Help me to bear out the fruit of Your spirit in response to being wounded. May forgiveness and love define me. Lord, in being wounded, stretch my faith, deepen my level of compassion, and weave a beautiful tapestry of unconditional love and forgiveness in my heart.
Amen!

Week Nine Menu

Parmesan Crusted Chicken

3 large chicken breasts, cut into 4 strips each

1½ sleeves Ritz crackers, crushed

⅓ cup Parmesan cheese, grated

1½ teaspoons garlic powder

Salt and pepper to taste

1½ sticks butter, melted

Preheat oven to 375°F. In sealed zipper-lock bag crush crackers with rolling pin. Add Parmesan cheese, garlic powder, salt, and pepper to crushed crackers. Toss in bag to blend. Dip chicken in melted butter then drop into in cracker mixture to coat. Remove and place on ungreased 9x13 baking sheet. Bake for 35 to 40 minutes.

Wild Rice with Grapes

2 tablespoons butter, divided

2 tablespoons sliced almonds

¼ cup green onions, chopped

1 (14 ounce) can chicken broth

3 tablespoons water

1 teaspoon salt

½ teaspoon pepper

⅔ cup wild rice

½ cup red grapes, halved

½ cup green grapes, halved

In a large saucepan, melt 1 tablespoon butter over medium heat; add almonds and cook 2 minutes. Stir occasionally until golden brown. Remove almonds and set aside. Melt remaining 1 tablespoon butter in pan. Add onions; cook, stirring constantly until tender. Add broth and next 3 ingredients; bring to a boil. Stir in rice; return to a boil. Cover and reduce heat and simmer 45 to 60 minutes or until rice is tender. Drain liquid. Stir in grapes. Sprinkle with almonds.

Easy Spinach Soufflé

1 (10 ounce) package chopped spinach, cooked and drained

¼ cup butter

¼ cup all-purpose flour

1 teaspoon salt

½ teaspoon black pepper

¾ cup half and half, or whole milk

1 cup white Cheddar cheese, shredded

2 tablespoons onion, chopped

1 tablespoon garlic, minced

4 eggs, room temperature, separated

Preheat oven to 375°F. In microwave-safe bowl, cook spinach according to package and drain. In large saucepan, melt butter over low heat; add flour and whisk until smooth and bubbly. Increase burner to medium heat; add salt, pepper, and half and half. Stir until thickened. Add in cheese, stir until melted. Remove from heat. Add spinach, onion, and garlic; gradually add egg yolks. Cool. In mixing bowl, on medium speed begin to whip egg whites, gradually increase speed to high until stiff peaks form. Gently fold egg whites into spinach, and pour into lightly greased 2 quart dish. Bake for 25 minutes until puffy and lightly golden.

Double Chocolate Brownies

2 (1 ounce) squares unsweetened chocolate, melted

2 (1 ounce) squares semisweet chocolate, melted

1 cup butter, softened

2 cups sugar

4 large eggs, room temperature

1 cup all-purpose flour

½ teaspoon salt

½ teaspoon baking soda

1 teaspoon vanilla extract

¾ cup semisweet chocolate morsels

Preheat oven to 350°F. Microwave chocolate squares in a small microwave-safe bowl at 50% power for 30 second intervals until melted. Stir chocolate until smooth. Beat butter and sugar at medium speed with an electric mixer until light and fluffy. Add eggs, one at a time, beating just until blended after each addition. Add melted chocolate, beating until blended. Add flour, salt, and baking soda beating at low speed just until blended. Stir in vanilla, and ½ cup chocolate morsels. Spread batter into a greased and floured 9x13 baking pan. Sprinkle with remaining morsels. Bake for 40 minutes or until set. Let cool completely before serving.

SHORT-CUTS...

- **PARMESAN CRUSTED CHICKEN:** If budget will allow, or you are short on time, use chicken tenders in place of chicken breasts. Crush the crackers and store in zipper-lock bag until needed.

- **PARMESAN CRUSTED CHICKEN:** This chicken dish can be prepared up to a day ahead of serving. Store sealed tightly in refrigerator until ready to bake.

- **WILD RICE WITH GRAPES:** Early in the day or the night before: Chop onion and slice grapes. Place in separate air-tight containers and refrigerate.

- **WILD RICE WITH GRAPES:** Can be prepared earlier in the day and reheated in the oven just prior to serving.

- **EASY SPINACH SOUFFLÉ:** This recipe can be prepared ahead of time up to adding the egg whites, which should not be done until just prior to baking. Store egg whites in covered dish until ready to whip and add to spinach dish.

- **DOUBLE CHOCOLATE BROWNIES:** Prepare and bake a day ahead. Store in air-tight container or cover baking pan with plastic wrap and foil.

HEALTHY TIPS...

- **PARMESAN CRUSTED CHICKEN:** Use hormone-free grain fed chicken. Use gluten-free crackers.

- **EIGHT HEALTH FACTS ON PARMESAN CHEESE:**

  1. Parmesan is a rich source of protein.
  2. Easily digestible compared to other cheese.
  3. Contains minimal amounts of lactose.
  4. Parmesan is a substantial source of minerals. It supplies a broad range of minerals, and it is particularly rich in calcium, phosphorus, selenium, sodium, and zinc.
  5. Contains a good supply of Omega-3.
  6. Provides a good amount of Vitamin K2 (Menaquinone).
  7. A good source of fat.
  8. Potential probiotic benefits.

- **WILD RICE WITH GRAPES:** Use organic chicken broth or homemade.

- **EASY SPINACH SOUFFLÉ:** Substitute low-fat milk for half and half. Dish will not be as creamy, but will contain less fat. If gluten intolerant, substitute almond flour for all-purpose flour.

- **DOUBLE CHOCOLATE BROWNIES:** The only healthy tip we can give you is to recommend that you not eat your hot brownie with a bowl of ice cream.

Friendship

A true friend is the greatest of all blessings.
—Francois de La Rochefoucauld

Friendship Introduction

*J*ust as there were seasons in creation, there are seasons in life. Some of us are in the season of singleness, some are in the young married season or the midlife season, while others are now into their senior years. I have noticed that in each and every season of my life, some of my friendships have changed due to changes in my circumstances, and some have remained steadfast, no matter the change in circumstances. My neighbor has friendships that she has maintained through Elementary school, Middle school, High School and college. What a rare blessing that is, considering our transient society.

Years ago, people were more likely to grow up and remain in the same town—having life-long friends. Now, with continual job changes and career advancements, people are uprooting and moving quite often. I was given two of my great-grandmother's journals. It has been fascinating to read through them since life was much different in the 1940's. She lived in the same town where she was born. Many of her social activities were spent with friends whom she had known all her life. They sat on the porch and talked, sang around the piano, played games, or listened to the radio—no television or iPhones then! My great grandmother and her friends walked through many seasons together. They spent a lifetime sharing the joys and the heartaches of life.

Due to my dad's pursuit of education, I did not grow up in one town, but moved quite often between the ages of a year and a half and thirteen. For the most part, I adapted well to new environments and because of that, I made friends easily. Children are resilient and can often adjust more easily to change than adults. Little did I know that having moved frequently as a child and having the ability to make friends easily would be beneficial when marrying Mark Dougharty. Over our forty-five years of marriage, the first fifteen involved moves to eight cities and seventeen different apartments or houses. Along the way and through different seasons of life, I made a lot of friends. I have lost touch with many over the years, but there are a few to whom I still send a Christmas card to each year. Just as the seasons come and go—so do friends!

Presently, I am in a unique season of life in my friendships and as a widow in my early 60's. In this new season, some friends have remained, and some have moved on. I find having married at seventeen years of age, and starting a family at the age of twenty, places me seasonally ahead of most of my friends. My oldest grandchild is at least ten years older than some of my friends' oldest grandchildren. Some of my younger friends have young adult children who are beginning their careers or getting married. I am in a season of singleness, yet my friends are married. Making friends as a widow is challenging because as much as I enjoy *girl time*, I also enjoy being with married couples—after all I was one for forty-five years!

In and out of every season, I know for sure, God is always there for us. The Bible says that He is our friend and that He sticks closer than a brother (or sister). No matter where we are living, and no matter the season we are passing through, we can be assured that He is with us!

But there is a friend who who sticks closer than a brother.
Proverbs 18:24 NIV

Day One

When I was a year and half old, my parents left their hometown and moved to Nashville, Tennessee, in order for my dad to earn a college degree. Then at four, we moved to another city and state for him to attend seminary. At 6, my dad was called to pastor a small church in Missouri and he began to pursue a graduate degree from Kansas University. In the middle of my third grade year, we moved to the Lawrence, Kansas, where the university was located. In Missouri, I had a wonderful third grade teacher and friends I had had since first grade. The new school and teacher in Lawrence did not prove to be a good move for me. It took a while for me to adjust. I am not sure I have ever forgiven my parents for uprooting me in the middle of my third grade year! We remained in Lawrence, Kansas until the end of my seventh grade year. My siblings and I were deeply rooted in the community, our church, and friendships there.

The move from Lawrence, Kansas back to Nashville, Tennessee, occurred between my seventh and eighth grade year. Making a major move at that age was challenging. Middle school is a difficult season in which to make new friends. This was especially true as I was going into an established area where the other kids had been together for years. When entering that type of school environment, often choosing friends is not an option—they choose you. Gratefully, my church environment was different from my school environment. In life, there will be those friends that we choose, and then those who chose us, as well as, those God chooses for us because He knows what we need. God chose two sweet and trustworthy **friends** for me through our church. We were inseparable. We shared the deepest matters of the heart with one another, well as deep as a Middle schooler's heart can be. They were just who I needed.

I heard a speaker once say, "To have a friend, you must first be a friend." In other words, do you desire to have friends? Then you must be a friend!

1. How would you define the word **friend**?

2. Write the dictionary definition of the word **friend**.

3. According to the dictionary definition, do you see yourself as a **friend** to others? **Yes**_____ **No**_____

4. Write the dictionary definition of the word **trustworthy**.

5. According to the dictionary definition, do you see yourself as a **trustworthy** friend to others? **Yes**_____ **No**_____

6. Do you have girls in your life that you would consider to be **trustworthy** friends? Name them below.

7. How have these friends proven to be **trustworthy**? Explain.

8. Write Proverbs 17:17.

This verse tells us that a friend **loves** at **all** times, but true deep and lasting friendships are often developed through **adversity**. Trouble, difficulty, hardship, suffering, and affliction are words that can be used in place of the word **adversity**.

9. Describe below a time when a friendship of yours was developed through **adversity**.

I believe friendships forged through **adversity** are often friendships God has chosen for us. He uses **adversity** to draw us to one another and forge deep friendships. God wants to use our story and the stories of others to spiritually sharpen and strengthen us, His children.

My story was different than Melanie's, but both our stories involved **adversity**. Just weeks after Mark passed away, I went to see Melanie and her husband, Tommie. A mutual friend had shared with me the details of their circumstances. I had not officially met them, but I had prayed for them for several months. Melanie had been Tommie's full-time caretaker over the months of his battle with ALS, as I had been for Mark with his illness.

She met me at the door that day. I sat and listened as they shared the journey they had walked over the prior months. Tommie, suffering with some of the same physical challenges as Mark had, asked about Mark's responses to many of these challenges. Their diseases were both neurological in nature, so there were some similarities. I shared with them our eleven year journey of Mark's illness and what God had taught us. Little did any of us know that just four weeks later Tommie would be admitted to the hospital for a mild case of pneumonia and a day later die from heart complications.

It was our individual **adversities** that drew Melanie and me together. Since the death of our husbands, God has given us a very special relationship—we understand the season that we both find ourselves in at this time. I can share my heart and pain with her—she gets it!

> 10. Fill in the blanks of the following verse: "The Lord is close to the _____ and saves those who are _____ in spirit" (Psalm 34:18 NIV).

A great example of a Biblical friendship forged through **adversity** is David and Jonathan. Theirs was an instant friendship. My friendship with Melanie is one such friendship. From the first time we met, we were immediately bonded with one another. Losing our husbands much earlier than we ever dreamed forged a deep friendship. She has been a **trustworthy** friend.

> 11. Have you ever met anyone that you knew immediately, due to similar circumstances that you were going to be good **friends**? What was it about that person and your circumstances that drew you instantly to her?

Read 1 Samuel 18:1-4 and 1 Samuel 20. In reading through David and Jonathan's story, we see a mutual respect and a fortified friendship that stood the test of great strain and even persecution. You will see the depth of their friendship and witness the support, protection, and unconditional love of these close-knit **friends**. David and Jonathan's friendship grew deeper with **adversity** and pain.

> 12. From the verses in 1 Samuel 18 and 20, what adjectives would you use in describing the friendship between David and Jonathan? List below.

Euripides, the Greek playwright, said, "Life has no blessing like a **prudent** friend." In other words, he was saying that having a **prudent** (wise, sensible, and cautious) friend is a blessing.[132]

13. What adjectives would you use to describe your friends and the blessing they are to you?

PONDER:

Walking with a friend in the dark is better than walking alone in the light.[133]
—Helen Keller

MEDITATE:

My command is this: Love each other as I have loved you. Greater love has no one than this: to lay down one's life for one's friends. You are my friends if you do what I command. I no longer call you servants, because a servant does not know his master's business. Instead, I have called you friends, for everything that I learned from my Father I have made known to you. You did not choose me, but I chose you and appointed you so that you might go and bear fruit—fruit that will last—and so that whatever you ask in my name the Father will give you. This is my command: Love each other.
John 15:12-16 NIV

PRAY:

Father, thank you for creating us, Your children, with a deep need for community and relationship. I am so thankful for the friends You have placed in my life. Help me to be a friend who loves unconditionally, serves continually, and encourages relentlessly.
Amen!

[132]Euripides, *Greek Playwriter*, https://www.brainyquote.com/quotes/euripides_149015
[133]Helen Keller, https://www.brainyquote.com/quotes/helen_keller_384608

Day Two

I was talking with a young lady about friendship. She said that in the midst of the pandemic of the COVID-19 she was seeing some of her friendships in a different light. It would seem that a pandemic brings out each of our unique personalities. She noted that her friends had responded according to their unique and individual personalities. In some cases, their responses made it clear why they were friends and what had brought them together in the first place—their **similarities**. In other cases, she was not sure how they had become friends based on the way they were handling the pandemic—their differences had surfaced.

God made us uniquely **different**. He **created** each of us according to His design. You might say He was the creator of *personality types*. Along with our being His unique design, the environment in which we grew up helped **shape** us into the unique individuals we are today, and this is also true for our friends.

1. What does Psalm 139:14 say about the way in which God created each individual?

Whether in a pandemic or just in the everyday circumstances of life, **differences** between friends are going to surface. **Differences** can actually be a good thing. If you are married, can you imagine living with someone exactly like you? Mark and I had **differing** personalities. Because of that, I found that we **complemented** one another. Although different, we had many things in common. We both enjoyed music, exercise, sports, and time as a family. Who we were at the core, the person God made us to be, never changed. In making friends, you will discover that you and your friends are very **different** from one another. Do not look at your **differences** as something negative, but allow those to be a positive part of your relationship. Friends are going to be **different** from one another, but when we consider what we have in common, most likely it is those things that brought us together in the first place.

> *Don't be afraid of being different, be afraid of being the same as everyone else.*
> *—Author Unknown*

Answer the questions below to aid you in considering your **differences** and how to handle them.

- Are your **differences** strictly the result of having opposite personality types? Can you accept her personality and allow it to sharpen and balance you?

- Are your **differences** in areas of moral beliefs? Are her moral beliefs so vastly opposite yours that you are wrongly influenced when in her presence?

- Do you have **differing** spiritual beliefs? Can you accept those **differences** without compromising your own beliefs?

- Are your **differences** due to being in separate seasons of life? Can you accept and even benefit from the season she is in? Can she benefit from the season you are in?

- Is this friendship **aiding** you in becoming a **better** person? In spending time with this friend, do you leave better for it? Does this friend spiritually sharpen you?

It is okay to be different as long as those differences are beneficial to your personal and spiritual growth. Differences should be valued as one of the many ways in which God sharpens us as individuals.

2. Fill in the blanks of the following verse: As iron _____ iron, so a friend _____ a friend" (Proverbs 27:17 NLT).

My friends and I have different personality types. Those differences are partly what drew us together. I have found over the years that **differences** in people can enhance a relationship. Having different personalities brings depth to a friendship—if we embrace and accept those **differences**. Let me illustrate this by showing you the difference in me and a couple of my friends. My personality tends to be accepting, trusting, and stable. I tend to be creative, optimistic, and supportive, but I can also be too willing to go along with others to keep the peace. Typically, I want everything to go smoothly and be without conflict, but I can also tend to be complacent, simplifying problems and minimizing anything upsetting. Stubbornness is also a struggle of mine. At my best: indomitable and all-embracing, I like to bring people together and heal conflicts.

My first friend displays a self-confident, strong, and assertive personality. She is protective, resourceful, straight-talking, and decisive, but can also come across as ego-centric and domineering. She struggles with controlling her environment, especially people, at times becoming confrontational and intimidating. She struggles with allowing herself to be vulnerable. At her best: self-mastering and great at using her strength to improve others' lives, becoming heroic, magnanimous, and inspiring.

My second friend displays an extroverted, optimistic, versatile, and spontaneous personality. She is playful, high-spirited, and practical, but can also misapply her many talents, becoming over-extended, scattered, and undisciplined. She seeks new and exciting experiences, but can become distracted and exhausted by staying on the go. Impatience and impulsiveness can be a problem at times. At her best: she focuses her talents on worthwhile goals, becoming appreciative, joyous, and satisfied.

Can you see how vastly different we are, yet how we can complement one another? Can you see how God uses us to sharpen one another personally and spiritually?

When I think of two women who were drawn together because of their circumstances and commonality yet were vastly **different**, I think of Naomi and Ruth.

Read the book of Ruth. It is a quick read. Now, let's look at the **differences** and **commonalities** of these two women.

DIFFERENCES:

- Naomi was an Ephrathites from Bethlehem in Judah. She was older, decisive, and had a take charge personality. She was tired and emotionally empty.

- Ruth was a Moabite. She was young, full of energy, quiet, humble, compassionate, and sacrificial.

COMMONALITY:

- Both were females

- They were each strangers in a foreign land

- Each woman left behind all that mattered to her

- They were both widowed with no seeming hope of ever being married again

- Both were poor, hungry, and needy

- Each was seeking safety and shelter

- Each woman was separated from her family

- Both sought to follow the God of Israel, Yahweh

- Each was in need of a Redeemer

Their friendship shows us the **value** of loyalty, of unconditional love, and self-sacrifice. Ruth didn't hesitate to share when Naomi was in need. This is the type of action that creates the strongest of friendships, and gives us a sense of security—we know that when we're in trouble, someone will be there for us.

Naomi and Ruth's **differences** were what sharpened and strengthened their friendship. Their **commonalties** were the *glue* that held their friendship together.

3. In considering one or two of your friendships, write below a few of your differences and a few things you have in common. Explain how each effects your friendship.

PONDER:

True friends face in the same direction, toward common projects, interests, goals.[134]
—C.S. Lewis

MEDITATE:

Bearing with one another and, if one has a complaint against another,
forgiving each other; as the Lord has forgiven you, so you also must forgive
Colossians 3:13 ESV

PRAY:

Father, You created each one of Your children uniquely. I am grateful for
Your wisdom in that, knowing that individual differences are beneficial because
they challenge, strengthen, and sharpen our relationships. Thank you for my friends,
for the differences and commonalities between us. My life is deeply enriched
by the women You have chosen to place into my life. May I be a friend who
walks with wisdom and integrity, honoring You and others.
Amen!

[134]C.S. Lewis, https://www.christianquotes.info/quotes-by-topic/quotes-about-friendship/

Day Three

Because Mark and I were married at such a young age, we had very little money to spend on rings. He was completing his senior year of college and I was graduating from High School a year early in order to get married. Mark purchased my wedding ring in the same store where he purchased a sleeping bag and small tent for a camping trip. That should tell you the quality of my ring!

Eleven years later, Mark surprised me with a new wedding ring. After we accepted Christ, our relationship was so vastly different that he wanted a new ring to represent our new relationship. The ring was absolutely beautiful. I had no idea what he had paid for it, but I knew it had to have been a large sum of money based on the quality of the ring and the jeweler he purchased it from.

Years later, we changed insurance companies and due to that they insisted on an appraisal of my ring. So, I took it to a local jeweler and secured a copy of the appraisal for the insurance agent. I decided to open the envelope to see the amount of the appraisal. I was shocked! I knew it was a nice ring, but after seeing what the jeweler deemed a fair appraisal amount, I **valued** my ring much more.

1. Write the definition of the word **value**.

2. To gain a better understanding of its full meaning, list below several synonyms for the word **value**.

It is strange how we fail to **value** the things we have and the people who make our lives full and complete until we no longer have them. Once my husband, Mark, passed away, I missed so many aspects of having him with me. I wish now that I had **valued** each one more and let him know more often that I truly **valued** him. I miss ...

- His friendship

- His wisdom and counsel

- His biblical knowledge that taught me so much (and answered all my questions)

- His companionship

- His hugs

- His cards and notes

- His thoughtfulness (he never missed a birthday, Mother's Day, anniversary, etc.)

- His prayers for me

- The ability to bring out the best in me

3. Define the word **significant** below.

---

*Do nothing from rivalry or conceit, but in humility count others more **significant** than yourselves.*
Philippians 2:3 ESV

Allow me the liberty of replacing the word **significant** in the verse above with the word **valuable**.

---

*Do nothing from rivalry or conceit, but in humility count others more **valuable** than yourselves.*
Philippians 2:3 (Dianne's translation)

---

4. In what ways would your relationships and friendships be different if you treated others as more **valuable** (**significant**) than yourself?

There is nothing on this earth more to be prized than true friendship.[135]
— Thomas Aquinas

[135]Thomas Aquinas, https://www.brainyquote.com/quotes/thomas_aquinas_163328

The word **prized** is a synonym for **valued**. We are to **prize** or **value** our friendships. When we **prize** something, we treat it with the utmost care; we protect it and guard over it. Have you noticed that we are willing to make sacrifices for the people we **prize**?

Read Daniel 1:3-21, 2:48-49

Daniel **valued** (**prized**) his friendship with Shadrach, Meshach, and Abednego so much that he requested King Nebuchadnezzar promote them to high positions. None of these four young men were willing to compromise their faith. They showed King Nebuchadnezzar through their actions and their relationship that they served a great God—the one and only God.

Daniel 2:49, "At Daniel's request, the king appointed Shadrach, Meshach, and Abednego to be in charge of all the affairs of the province of Babylon, while Daniel remained in the king's court" (NLT).

5. List several ways you can show each of your friends how **valuable** they are to you and what they have added to your life.

You will probably never enter a fiery furnace as Jesus did to show your friend how **valuable** she is to you. But, there are so many ways you can express your appreciation for her and show her how **valuable** she is to you. Don't wait until your friend moves away or becomes terminally ill before letting her know how **valued** your friendship is and how **valuable** she is as a person.

PONDER:

Many people will walk in and out of your life,
but only true friends leave footprints in your heart.[136]
—Eleanor Roosevelt

MEDITATE:

Treat others the same way you want them to treat you.
Luke 6:31 NASB

PRAY:

Lord, each and every one of Your children holds great value.
Help me to have a humble spirit and to treat others more
valuable than myself. May all my friends know the value they are
in my life and the joy they have brought to me. Because we are
each valued by You, Father, may we value one another as
much as You have prized and valued us.
Amen!

 [136]Eleanor Roosevelt, https://www.goodreads.com/quotes/40249-many-people-will-walk-in-and-out-of-your-life

Day Four

Thus far, we have discussed having **trustworthy** friends, friendships that have been forged through adversity and appreciating the **differences** between us and our friends. We have looked at **commonalities** between women that can lead to friendship, and talked about **valuing** the person and the friendships we currently have.

In a conversation with my older daughter, I asked her if there was anything she would say to women on friendship? She said, "Well, if I were writing on the topic of friendship, I would have to talk about social media and how texting and emailing have killed friendships." So, I asked, "In what way?" She responded, "When I was a young mom with little ones, my friends in the same stage of life, would call while the kids were napping or we would meet at a local playground or Chick-fil-A. None of us cared how many children the other one had or whether they were boys or girls. I don't think we were even that concerned about having a lot in common, we just needed a place to reconnect with women in the same stage of life and allow our kids time to play with one another. We were desperate for adult conversation and friendship. Now, everyone communicates through Facebook, Twitter, or texting. There is little **face-to-face** connecting anymore. But, God made us for community and relationship—**face-to-face**. He did not make us for isolation and seclusion. Look at how the 2020 pandemic quarantine affected people. Suicides increased along with domestic and child abuse. We need people, we need **face-to-face** interaction—we need **friends**."

God created us to be in relationship with Himself and with others in friendship, marriage, family, society, and the church.

1. What does Romans 5:10-11 say about our relationship with God? How was that relationship secured?

Christ took our sins upon himself and took our punishment by dying on the cross.
Now we can rejoice in God. Through faith in Christ's work, we become close to
*God, **friends**, rather than being enemies or outcasts.*[137]
NLT Parallel Study Bible

God **chose** us to be His own, to have companionship and friendship with Him. In return, there comes a point in each individual's life when she must choose between the world, self, or Him. In **choosing** Him, we receive the deepest of friendships with the Creator of all mankind—God himself!

[137]*NLT Parallel Study Bible* (Carol Stream, Illinois: Tyndale House Publishing, 2011). P. 2122

2. What does Ecclesiastes 4:9-12 say about the **value** of companionship or **friendship**?

Life is designed for companionship not isolation, for intimacy, not loneliness.
Some people prefer isolation, thinking they cannot trust anyone. We are not here
on earth to serve ourselves, however, but to serve God and others. Don't isolate
yourself and try to go it alone. Seek companionships; be a team player.[138]
NLT Parallel Study Bible

When we seek companionship, we must be wise and discerning about those we choose as friends.

3. Read the following quote and list ways in which choosing the wrong types of friends has impacted your life, and in some cases, done irreparable damage.

---

*The friends we **choose** can change our lives forever. If we **choose** the wrong*
type of friend, their influence can corrupt us and cause irreparable damage.
—Author Unknown

There are basic relational needs that women have which can only be met in female friends. God created us for companionship, relationship, community, and friendship. We are communicators, we are relational beings who need women to talk with, and at times, those who will be attentive and listen to us.

God had one major prerequisite for being a friend to you and me—we must have accepted His Son as our Lord and Savior. What should our prerequisites be for **choosing** friends? As Christian women, what we are looking for in the women we **choose** to have as friends should look different than those that the world is looking for in a friend.

[138]*NLT Parallel Study Bible* (Carol Stream, Illinois: Tyndale House Publishing, 2011). P. 1144

Consider the following questions when **choosing** women to be your friend:

A. Is she self-centered? Yes____ No____

B. Is she manipulative and controlling? Yes____ No____

C. Does she always have to be right? Yes____ No____

D. Does she accept you, warts and all? Yes____ No____

E. If she is married: Is she honoring of her mother-in-law? <u>Note</u>: If she is single, is she honoring of the other women in her life? Yes____ No____

F. If she is married: Is she honoring of your husband? <u>Note</u>: If she is single: Is she honoring of her male friends or the young men she dates? Yes____ No____

G. If she is married: Is she devoted to her marriage? Yes____ No____ <u>Note</u>: If she is single: Is she devoted to her family and other friends? Yes____ No____

H. Is she compassionate? Yes____ No____

I. Is she there for you when life is hard? Yes____ No____

J. Is she forgiving? Yes____ No____

K. Does she give freely of her time and resources to those in need? Yes____ No____

L. Does she challenge you to go deeper in your walk with the Lord? Yes____ No____

M. Does she pray for you? Yes____ No____

N. Do you see radiance, warmth, and something different in her that causes you to want to spend time with her? Yes____ No____

O. Does she consistently have a negative outlook on life? Yes____ No____

If the answers to A, B, C, and O were yes, I would recommend that you seriously consider whether a friendship with this particular person is emotionally and spiritually healthy for you.

4. Fill in the blanks of the following verse. "Walk with the _____ and become _____; associate with _____ and get in _____" (Proverbs 13:20 NLT).

Let's look at a biblical friendship that involved a **choice**—Elisha's friendship with Elijah. As you will see in this story, innumerable blessings will be the result of **choosing** wisely those we desire to have as friends.

Read 2 Kings chapter 2.

Elijah was the well-known prophet of Israel. He called down the fires of heaven, defeating the prophets of Baal and through his prayers he caused a drought in Israel for three years. In order to help him carry out his work, God sent Elijah a **friend**, and eventual successor, the younger Elisha.

Their devout friendship was an example of making a purposeful **choice** in seeking out a friend. Elisha attached himself to Elijah, not wanting to be separated from him. In responding to Elijah's declaration that he was leaving for Bethel, Elisha exclaims, "As the Lord lives, and as you yourself live, I will not leave you." Elisha was completely devoted to his **friend**, Elijah, his mentor, because he knew the older man would make an excellent guide.

Let those be thy choicest companions who have made Christ their chief companion.[139] —Thomas Brooks

5. Explain the quote above and why this statement is especially true in the life of a Christian.

It is important to **choose** friends who are wise, holy, and passionate about what they do—after all, we often become like our peers. In placing himself close, **face-to-face** with Elijah, Elisha prepared himself for his calling. Through Elijah, he found the mentor and **friend** who would help him become a worthy prophet and servant of God.

PONDER:

*Surround yourself with people who strengthen your character,
and remove yourself from people who compromise your character.*[140]
—Helen Keller

MEDITATE:

The righteous choose their friends carefully, but the way of the wicked leads them astray.
Proverbs 12:26 NIV

PRAY:

*Lord, You designed us for face-to-face relationships. The world is drawing us
away from who You created us to be. You did not create us for isolation,
but for community, companionship, and friendship. Help me to choose wisely
those I befriend. May I be a wise, discerning, kind, loving, and available friend
to the women You have placed within my life, those who are such a blessing to me.
Amen!*

[139]Thomas Brooks, https://deeperchristianquotes.com/how-to-choose-friends-thomas-brooks
[140]Dave Willis, https://www.goodreads.com/author/show/7060824.Dave_Willis

Day Five

For several years, every Wednesday at 5:45 a.m. my husband, Mark, would leave to attend a book study group led by his **friend**, Spence. As his disease progressed, he was no longer able to drive himself. Each week we would rise at 4:50 a.m. so I could shave and dress him in order to be ready when his ride arrived around 5:45 a.m. Without fail, for almost two years, Mark's friend, Dwight, would arrive to pick him up. If he were going to be out of town, he would arrange for Spence or Bart to pick Mark up.

Week in and week out these three men loved, served, and sacrificed their time for Mark. They would lift him from his wheelchair into their vehicles, load his wheelchair in the back, put his seatbelt on, and make sure he had his notes for that week's lesson. Many times as we sat waiting, we talked about the incredible gift their coming to get Mark was to both of us. It gave me some time alone, and it gave Mark time with **friends** and a reason to keep on fighting the disease that was so desperately wanting to consume his body.

A friend is defined as a person whom one knows and with whom one has a bond of mutual affection.

The word **mutual** means *having the same specified relationship to each other, and affection means a gentle feeling of fondness or liking.*

In other words, if you have a mutual respect, admiration, and fondness or liking toward a person and that person reciprocates those feelings, you are **friends**. Dwight, Spence, and Bart were just that to Mark—**friends**!

According to an article written by Wesley Baines, "There are three essential traits that psychologists deem necessary for friendships to thrive: displayed love, loyalty, and emotional openness."[141]

Today, we are going to look at these three traits, the first being **displayed love**.

1. Write Romans 12:10 in the NIV below.

2. In your opinion, which comes first in a friendship honor or love? Explain.

We could argue the answer to that question with some saying that you must display **love** before you can show honor and others saying that you must honor a person before you can truly **love** them. So, who is correct?

The word **love** is sometimes synonymous for **honor**. In Romans 12:10, Paul commands us to "Be devoted to one another in **love**. **Honor** one another above yourselves." It is only by being imbued with humility by the power of the Holy Spirit that we can esteem, honor, and unconditionally **love** others.

3. Did you know that **love** is a verb and not a noun? A noun is a person, place, or thing. What is a verb? What does a verb require?

---

*In the New Testament, **love** is more of a verb than a noun. It has more to do with acting than with feeling. The call to **love** is not so much a call to a certain state of feeling as it is to a quality of action.*[142]
—*R. C. Sproul*

---

4. The first trait is **displayed love**. In what ways do friends **display** love toward one another?

Over the eleven year journey of Mark's battle with Multiple Systems Atrophy, our friends **displayed** their **love** in many ways. Some sat with Mark in order to give me a break; one couple knew of Mark's love for music, so they brought dinner, and sat around his bed and sang. One friend and her family came and caroled around his bed at Christmas. Over the years, the **love** of our friends was **displayed** through their actions!

5. The second trait in developing a thriving friendship is **loyalty**. Write the definition of **loyalty** below.

 [142]R.C Sproul, https://www.whatchristianswanttoknow.com/23-great-r-c-sproul-quotes

I think the word **loyal** is a strong and powerful word. **Loyalty** endures over time and through pain and heartache. A **loyal** friend does not need to fully understand what God is doing in your life or why in order to remain **loyal**.

6. The synonyms below help clarify the word **loyal**. Fill in the blank to complete the word.

Faith__ __ __ness   Trust__ __ __ __ __iness

De__ __ tion   De__ __ __ __ ability

Commit__ __ __ __   Stead__ __ __ __ness

7. The third trait in developing a thriving friendship is **emotional openness**. How would you define **emotional openness**?

I would define it as: T R A N S P A R E N C Y and unconditional A C C E P T A N C E. I am not sure what I would have done along our journey, and since, if not for the **friends** on whose shoulders I could cry, into whose hearts I could pour my pain, and by whose words I was comforted and encouraged.

> *It is best to be with those in time, that we hope to be with in eternity.*[143]
> —*Thomas Fuller*

Certainly the three traits mentioned today are vital in developing a **friendship** that will thrive, but there is one more **key trait** that the psychologists failed to mention. That key trait is **Jesus**.

> "Every day my dad prayed that God would put three people in his path that he could talk to about God. God never failed in answering that prayer. One day my dad was driving home from work when he saw a farmer in a field motioning to my dad to turn down a country lane. So my dad did. He got out of his car, walked onto the front porch of the small farmhouse, and before he could knock on the door, a large man in overalls came to the door.
>
> 'Did God send you to talk to me?' the man asked. 'Yes, He did.' my dad said. The man invited my dad into the house. As my dad sat down on the couch, he noticed a shot gun on the coffee table. 'I was sitting here with my shotgun trying to think of one reason why I should live another day.' The man said in a defeated tone.

'I can give you a good reason. God loves you, and I do too.' my dad said back. The man broke down. His life had been hard. He had more problems than **friends**. By the end of the afternoon, my dad was his **friend**. By the end of the evening, **Jesus** was his **friend**. My dad had thousands of conversations like that one. My dad had thousands of **friends** who became **friends** with **Jesus**."[144] —Jon Weece

What did David and Jonathan, Naomi and Ruth, Daniel, Shadrach, Meshach, and Abednego, and Elijah and Elisha have in common? **JESUS**!

When Jesus is the common denominator between friends, displayed love, loyalty, and emotional openness are a natural outflow.

8. Do you have a **friend** with whom **Jesus** is not a common denominator in your relationship? Prayerfully ask God for an opportunity to share with her about the greatest friendship you have ever had—your friendship with **Jesus**. Write your prayer below.

PONDER:

He is your friend who pushes you nearer to God.[145]
—Abraham Kuyper

MEDITATE:

Above all, love each other deeply, because love covers over a multitude of sins.
1 Peter 4:8 NIV

PRAY:

Father, thank you for being my intimate friend and for
blessing my life with friendships. You have given me friends
for companionship and to enrich my life along this journey
—for that I am grateful. Help me to be a friend who continually
displays love, is loyal, and one who is transparent and accepting.
May those closest to me know that You are my best and most intimate
friend, and may that friendship be the solidifier of all my relationships.
Amen!

[144]Jon Weece, *Jesus Prom*, (Nashville, Tennessee: Thomas Nelson, 2014). P. 56-57
[145]Abraham Kuyper, christian-quotes.ochristian.com/Friendship-Quotes/page-10.shtml

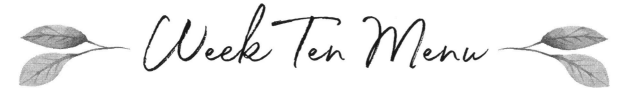

Week Ten Menu

Momma's Brisket

1 cup catsup

1 cup ginger ale

1 package onion soup mix

1 teaspoon spicy steak sauce

Salt and pepper

1 (2½ to 3 pounds) beef brisket

¼ cup red wine vinegar

Combine the first 5 ingredients in a large Dutch oven. Add the brisket and turn to coat with sauce. Over medium heat, bring to a slow boil. Reduce heat to simmer and add red wine vinegar. Cover and simmer for 2 hours. If necessary, at the end of cooking time if sauce has been reduced too much, add ¼ cup water. Note: A Dutch oven is a heavy pot with a lid that is used in the oven. It cooks slowly so flavors develop and tougher cuts of meat can slowly braise and become tender. Our modern answer to the Dutch oven is a slow cooker or *Crock-Pot*. A slow cooker and a *Crock-Pot* are the same thing. *Crock-Pot* is a brand name. If you don't have either, use a good stock pot with a tight lid. Keep the heat on low and check the liquid level often.

Make-Ahead Ranch Mashed Potatoes

4 cups potatoes, peeled and cubed

⅓ cup water

½ teaspoon salt

1 cup half and half, divided

⅓ cup sour cream

1½ teaspoons Ranch dressing mix

4 tablespoons butter, melted

Preheat oven to 375°F. In 2 quart pan, place potatoes, water, and salt. Cook over high heat until water comes to a boil. Reduce heat to medium-low. Cover and cook until potatoes are fork tender (not mushy). Drain. Mash potatoes with potato masher or hand mixer; gradually add ⅓ cup half and half. Stir in sour cream and dressing mix. Spread potato mixture evenly into a 1½ quart casserole dish. Pour remaining half and half over potatoes. DO NOT MIX. Top with butter. Cover; refrigerate 4 hours or overnight. Bake uncovered for 20 minutes. Stir and continue baking for 20 to 30 minutes or until heated through.

Yummy Carrots

2 cups water

1 bag carrots, peeled and sliced

6 tablespoons butter

⅔ cup brown sugar

1⅓ cups orange juice

½ teaspoon cinnamon

¼ teaspoon nutmeg

Pre-heat oven to 375°F. Place sliced carrots in 2 cups of water in large saucepan and bring to a boil. Cook until carrots are slightly tender, remove and drain. Mix in butter, brown sugar, orange juice, and spices. Mix well, cook over low heat until sugar dissolves and carrots are coated. Spread onto cookie sheet and bake for 20 to 25 minutes until lightly brown. Serve hot.

Apple Cobbler A La Mode

6 cups cooking apples, peeled and sliced

1½ cups chopped walnuts, divided

½ cup firmly packed brown sugar

1 teaspoon ground cinnamon

1 cup all-purpose flour

1 cup sugar

1 teaspoon baking powder

¼ teaspoon salt

¼ teaspoon ginger

½ cup half and half

½ cup butter, melted

1 egg, beaten

Vanilla Ice Cream

Preheat oven to 350°F. Place sliced apples topped with 1 cup chopped walnuts, brown sugar, and cinnamon in a large 9x13 baking dish. Set aside. Combine flour, sugar, baking powder, salt, and ginger in a large bowl; stir well. Combine half and half, melted butter, and egg; stir well. Add liquid ingredients to dry ingredients, stirring just until blended. Pour batter over apple mixture; sprinkle with remaining ½ cup chopped walnuts. Bake for 45 minutes to 1 hour or until lightly browned. To serve, spoon warm cobbler into individual serving bowls. Top with vanilla ice cream. Note: Granny Smiths apples recommended. Optional: Drizzle with caramel sauce.

SHORT-CUTS...

- **MOMMA'S BRISKET:** Marinade can be made 8 to 24 hours ahead. Up to 24 hours in advance of cooking, place brisket in zipper-lock bag turning to cover with marinade. Refrigerate until time to cook.

- **MAKE-AHEAD RANCH MASHED POTATOES:** Peel potatoes and carrots earlier in the day. Place in individual bowls of cold water and refrigerate.

- **YUMMY CARROTS:** Instead of peeling whole carrots, substitute mini carrots.

- **APPLE COBBLER A LA MODE:** Peel apples ahead and preserve in lemon juice or Sprite.

- **APPLE COBBLER A LA MODE:** This dish can be prepared and partially baked earlier in the day. While eating dinner complete the baking process. Cobbler can also be baked earlier in the day and served at room temperature or individual servings heated in the microwave prior to serving.

- Note: You can reduce much of your preparation time by using a food processor. It chops and slices vegetables in a fraction of the time it would take to do it by hand. The only vegetables that do not do well using this process are moist vegetables. Example: Mushrooms, tomatoes, and peppers.

HEALTHY TIPS...

- **MOMMA'S BRISKET:** Use an organic catsup with little to no added sugar or sugar-free catsup.

- **MOMMA'S BRISKET:** Because the Ginger Ale has sugar, but is a necessary ingredient, use one of these sugar-free choices for the steak sauce: G Hughes Smokehouse Sugar-free Steak Sauce or Primal Kitchen Organic Sugar Free Steak Sauce.

- **MAKE-AHEAD RANCH MASHED POTATOES:** Make your own ranch dressing mix. Note: Recipe in Week 4.

- **YUMMY CARROTS:** For carrot dish use organic low sugar orange juice or squeeze your own.

- **YUMMY CARROTS:** In carrot dish and apple cobbler, substitute raw honey in place of sugar. Note: Health problems can result when there is an abundance of sugar in your diet. Refined sugar has been shown to wreak havoc in the control of diabetes and hypoglycemia. It also raises triglycerides and the risk of dental cavities and obesity. It can lay a foundation for sugar dependency and abuse; it can set a craving process in motion. Local raw honey has many health benefits and should be worked into your diet when possible. But, all sugars should be limited. Equivalents: $\frac{2}{3}$ cup brown sugar = $\frac{2}{3}$ cup raw honey.

- **APPLE COBBLER A LA MODE:** Use unbleached all-purpose flour. To add fiber mix in $\frac{1}{4}$ cup of oats to batter before pouring over sliced apples.

- **APPLE COBBLER A LA MODE:** When substituting raw honey for sugar, add honey to the liquids called for in recipe. Equivalents: 1 cup sugar = $\frac{1}{4}$ cup raw honey.

Appetizers

Hot Black Bean and Corn Dip

1 (15 ounce) can yellow corn, drained

1 (15 ounce) can black beans, drained and rinsed

1 (10 ounce) can Rotel, drained

1 (8 ounce) cream cheese, softened, cubed

1 teaspoon chili powder

½ teaspoon garlic powder

½ teaspoon cumin

Pinch ground cayenne pepper

1 cup Mexican cheese, shredded, divided

Preheat oven to 350°F. In a medium sized bowl, add the corn, black beans, Rotel, cream cheese, chili powder, garlic powder, cumin, cayenne and ½ cup of shredded cheese. Stir together to incorporate. Pour into 8x8 baking dish and spread evenly. Top with remaining ½ cup of cheese. Bake for approximately 25 to 30 minutes, until cheese has melted, and mixture is bubbly. Serve with tortilla chips.

Cheese Ball

1 (8 ounce) sharp Cheddar cheese, shredded

1 (8 ounce) cream cheese, softened

1 cup mayonnaise

4 green onions, chopped

1 cup slivered almonds

TOPPING:

⅔ to ¾ cup orange marmalade

4 slices of bacon, cooked and crumbled

In large mixing bowl, blend Cheddar cheese, cream cheese and mayonnaise until incorporated. Stir in onions and almonds. Roll into ball. In small bowl, melt marmalade in microwave. Once cooled, pour over cheese ball and top with crumbled bacon.

Pimento Cheese Sausage Balls

1 pound breakfast sausage (mild or hot)

1 (12 ounce) jar Pimento cheese

2¼ cups Bisquick

Dash of paprika

Dash of red pepper

Preheat oven to 375°F. Add sausage and Pimento cheese to a large mixing bowl and mix to combine. Add Bisquick and spices. Stir until combined into a large ball. Scoop and roll into 1-inch balls. Place balls on lightly sprayed baking sheet. Bake for 20 to 25 minutes, until golden on top. Store in airtight container in refrigerator for up to a week.

Chicken Nut Puffs

1 cup all-purpose flour

1 tablespoon chopped parsley

2 teaspoons celery seed

½ teaspoon paprika

⅛ teaspoon ground red pepper

1 cup chicken broth

½ cup butter

2 teaspoons Worcestershire sauce

4 eggs, room temperature

5 ounces cooked chicken breast, shredded

¼ cup toasted almonds, chopped

Preheat oven to 400°F. In mixing bowl, combine flour, parsley, celery seed, paprika, and red pepper. Set aside. In saucepan over medium heat, combine chicken broth, butter, and Worcestershire sauce. Bring to a boil. Reduce heat to low and add in flour mixture and stir until incorporated and dough leaves the sides of pan. Remove from stove and cool. Add eggs one at a time, beating until smooth. Add in chicken and almonds. Drop by teaspoon and bake for 15 to 18 minutes or until golden brown. Remove from baking sheet immediately and serve hot.

Joy's Ham Delights

2 (12 ounce) packages Hawaiian dinner rolls

¾ cup butter, melted

2 tablespoons Dijon mustard

1½ teaspoons Worcestershire sauce

1 tablespoon dried minced onion

1 teaspoon garlic powder

1 pound deli ham, thinly sliced

1 pound Swiss cheese, thinly sliced

Preheat oven to 375°F. Slice rolls in half and place bottom halves in buttered 9x13 baking dish. In medium size mixing bowl, combine melted butter, mustard, Worcestershire sauce, onion, and garlic powder. Set aside. Place a slice of ham and cheese on each roll half in baking dish. Place tops of rolls on each. Brush each roll with butter mixture. Cover dish with foil and bake for 15 to 20 minutes until heated through.

Creamy Shrimp Dip

1 (8 ounce) package cream cheese, softened

½ cup mayonnaise

½ cup tomato ketchup

½ teaspoon lemon juice

1 teaspoon Worcestershire sauce

Pinch salt

1 small onion, minced

1 cup shrimp, deveined, peeled, chopped

In mixing bowl, mix cream cheese, mayonnaise, ketchup, lemon juice, and Worcestershire sauce until well blended. Add salt and onion. Fold in shrimp. Chill for one hour before serving.

Walnut Basil Pastries

16 frozen 14x18 inch Phyllo sheets, thawed in refrigerator

¾ cup butter, melted

8 (1 ounce) slices Provolone cheese, quartered

Walnut Ricotta Spread

14 dried tomatoes in oil, drain and chop

Fresh basil sprigs for garnish

Preheat oven to 425°F. Place 2 sheets of phyllo on work surface, keeping the remaining sheets covered. Brush sheet with butter. Cut buttered phyllo sheets lengthwise into 4 equal strips about 3½ inch wide. Place 1 piece Provolone, folded if necessary, onto one end of strip. Spoon a tablespoon Walnut Ricotta spread over cheese; top with a few pieces of dried tomato. Take one strip at a time, fold bottom corner of phyllo over filling, forming a triangle. Continue folding back and forth to end of strip. Lightly brush phyllo triangle with butter to seal. Repeat process with remaining phyllo, (2 sheets at a time), butter, Provolone cheese, Walnut Ricotta spread, and dried tomatoes. Place pastries on ungreased baking sheet for 10 to 11 minutes or until evenly browned. Garnish if desired.

WALNUT RICOTTA SPREAD:

2 small garlic cloves

1 cup Ricotta cheese

¾ cup Parmesan cheese

1 teaspoon sugar

½ cup walnuts, chopped

12 fresh basil leaves, sliced

1 tablespoon olive oil

½ teaspoon salt

¼ teaspoon pepper

With food processor running, drop garlic cloves through chute; process until minced. Add cheeses and sugar; process until smooth, stopping to scrape down sides. Add walnuts, basil, olive oil, salt, and pepper; process until blended.

White Chocolate Crunch

2 cups Corn Chex cereal

2 cups Golden Grahams cereal

2 cups Honey Nut Cheerios cereal

1 cup salted peanuts

4 handfuls mini pretzels

1 (16 ounce) package white chocolate

In large mixing bowl, place cereals, peanuts, and pretzels. Toss to mix. Melt white chocolate according to package instructions. Pour over cereal mixture and stir until well coated. Pour mixture onto a piece of parchment paper and spread making a thin layer. Allow to dry (about 30 minutes). Break into pieces. Store in airtight container.

Salted Chocolate Pretzel Toffee

Mini pretzels, broken into smaller pieces (as many as it takes to cover your pan)

4 cups chocolate chips (milk, dark, or white chocolate)

1 cup unsalted butter

1 cup light brown sugar

Sea salt

Preheat oven to 375°F. Line cookie sheet with aluminum foil or parchment paper. Set aside. Place pretzels in zipper-lock bag. Using a rolling pin break the pretzels into smaller pieces, but not into crumbs. Cover the pan in a layer of pretzels pieces. In a small saucepan over medium heat, combine the butter and brown sugar. When mixture begins to gently simmer and bubble, cook for 3 minutes. <u>Do not stir</u>. Pour the butter and sugar mixture over the pretzels and bake in oven for 5 minutes. Place the pan on a cooling rack and immediately sprinkle chocolate chips evenly over the top. Wait 2 minutes. Using a spatula, spread chocolate over the toffee. Sprinkle with sea salt. Let the toffee cool completely and break into pieces. To advance the cooling process, place pan in the refrigerator.

Entrées

Apple-Pecan Stuffed Chicken Breasts

1 (4 ounce) package Goat cheese, crumbled

½ Granny Smith apples, peeled and chopped

¼ cup pecans, toasted and chopped

1 tablespoon fresh parsley, chopped

6 (8 ounce) chicken breasts, skinless, boneless

½ teaspoon salt

½ teaspoon pepper

4 tablespoons butter, soft, divided

1 garlic clove, minced

2 tablespoons all-purpose flour

1 cup chicken broth

⅔ cup white wine vinegar

2 tablespoons fresh parsley, chopped

⅛ teaspoon ground pepper

Preheat oven to 450°F. In small bowl, combine first 4 ingredients. Using a sharp knife, cut a slit (2 to 3 inches long, do not cut in half) in the thick side of each chicken breast to form a pocket. Spoon 1 rounded tablespoon goat cheese mixture into each pocket. Pinch edges to seal and push 2 to 3 toothpicks along slit to secure pocket. Sprinkle chicken evenly with ½ teaspoon salt and ½ teaspoon pepper. In large skillet over medium heat, melt 2 tablespoons of butter; add 3 chicken breasts. Cook 2 to 3 minutes on each side until lightly browned. Grease 9x13 baking dish and transfer chicken from skillet to dish. Repeat procedure with remaining chicken. Bake for 20 minutes, until chicken is done. In skillet over medium heat, melt remaining 1 tablespoon butter in pan drippings; add garlic. Whisk in flour and stir for 1 minutes. Gradually whisk in chicken broth and white wine vinegar, cook for 8 to 10 minutes or until thickened and bubbly. Stir in parsley and ⅛ teaspoon pepper. Spoon sauce over baked chicken breast and serve.

Roasted Chili Rubbed Salmon

4 (4 ounce) salmon, skinless

1 tablespoon olive oil

½ cup red onion, coarsely chopped

2½ teaspoons chili powder, divided

1 (14 ounce) bag frozen corn kernels

1 cup mixed bell peppers, cut in strips

¼ cup fresh cilantro, chopped

1 teaspoon salt

¼ teaspoon black pepper

Preheat oven to 450°F. In 10-inch skillet, heat oil over medium heat. Add onion and cook 2 minutes until tender. Add 1½ teaspoons chili powder and stir until blended. Add corn and bell peppers; cook until crisp tender. Stir in cilantro. Spread even layer of vegetables in 9x13 baking dish. Sprinkle remaining chili powder over salmon. Place salmon chili side up on vegetables. Sprinkle with salt and pepper. Bake for 20 minutes, until salmon flakes.

Spicy Rubbed Pork Tenderloin

1 tablespoon each, ground ginger, coriander, garlic powder, and onion powder

½ teaspoon cayenne

2 pounds pork tenderloin

1 tablespoon olive oil

½ cup low-sodium soy sauce

1 tablespoon Sriracha sauce (chili or hot sauce)

2 tablespoons honey

1 tablespoon cornstarch

¼ cup fresh cilantro, chopped

Preheat oven to 425°F. Line rimmed baking sheet with foil and coat with nonstick spray or use parchment paper. Set aside. In small bowl, mix ginger, coriander, garlic powder, onion powder, and cayenne. Pat the pork dry then rub with spice mixture covering all the meat. Heat olive oil in large sauté pan or skillet. Carefully add tenderloin, bending to fit pan if necessary. Sear 2 minutes per side. Move pork to prepared baking sheet and roast for 30 minutes, ensuring pork reaches a safe internal temperature of 145°F. Remove from oven, cover and allow to rest for 10 minutes before serving. Top with sauce and serve.

SAUCE:

In small bowl, whisk together soy sauce, Sriracha, and honey. Stir in cornstarch. Transfer to small skillet and bring to a simmer. Remove from heat and add cilantro. Drizzle over tenderloin slices and serve.

Pan-Seared Cod Pecan Filets

½ cup Panko bread crumbs

½ cup pecans, finely chopped

⅓ cup flour

1 teaspoon each baking powder, salt, ground pepper, and paprika

½ cup buttermilk

2 tablespoons butter

1½ pounds Cod fillets

1 lemon, cut in wedges for serving

In small bowl, combine panko crumbs and pecans. In additional bowl, combine flour, baking powder, salt, pepper, and paprika; mix well. In a third bowl, add buttermilk. Use one fillet at a time, dust in flour mixture and shake of excess. Dip fillet in buttermilk to evenly coat and drain excess. Dredge in pecan mixture, coating thoroughly. In large skillet, melt butter over medium heat; add fillets and cook on each side for 2 to 3 minutes, or until fish is golden, flakes with a fork and reaches a safe internal temperature of 145°F. Serve with fresh lemon wedges, refrigerate any leftovers.

Pinwheel Round Steak Strips

2 (1 pound) boneless top round steaks, 1-inch thick

Salt and pepper

1 (8 ounce) package cream cheese, softened

3 tablespoons fresh chives, chopped, divided

1½ teaspoons lemon-pepper seasoning

2 garlic cloves, minced

Preheat oven to 375°F. Place steaks in zipper-lock bag, using a meat mallet tenderize the steaks. Cut each steak lengthwise into 4 strips (about 1½ inches wide). Sprinkle with salt and pepper. Place cream cheese in a small bowl. With mixer, beat at medium speed until creamy. Stir in 2 tablespoons of chives, lemon pepper seasoning, and garlic. Spread cream cheese mixture down center of each strip of meat. Roll strips, jelly roll fashion, and secure ends with wooden picks. Cut slices and place pinwheels in shallow baking dish. Transfer pinwheels to a rack in a roasting pan. Cover and bake for 20 minutes. Uncover and bake an additional 5 to 10 minutes or to desired degree of doneness. Remove wooden picks. Transfer pinwheels to serving platter and garnish with 1 tablespoon chopped fresh chives.

Ginger's Rosemary Garlic Chicken

6 boneless skinless chicken breasts

4 tablespoons lemon juice

2 cloves garlic, minced

2 tablespoons fresh rosemary, divided

In zipper-lock bag, combine lemon juice, garlic, and rosemary. Add chicken breast and marinate overnight.

½ pound Pancetta, chopped

1 shallot, chopped

1 cup mushrooms, sliced (Optional)

1 (16 ounce) Marsala cooking wine

1 (16 ounce) heavy whipping cream

1 tablespoon olive oil

1 (1 pound) box Angel hair pasta

2 tablespoons fresh parsley, chopped for garnish

In heavy skillet, brown Pancetta, shallots, and mushrooms until Pancetta is crisp and fat rendered. Remove from skillet. Deglaze pan with Marsala, stirring well. Add heavy cream and bring to a low boil. Reduce heat and simmer 10 minutes to thicken. In large skillet over medium heat, add 1 tablespoon olive oil. Salt and pepper chicken breasts, place in skillet. Cook 5 to 6 minutes on each side until golden brown and cooked through. Boil pasta according to directions on package. Drain and toss in cream sauce. Add Pancetta mixture. Top with chicken. Garnish with parsley.

Creamy Salmon Filets

1 cup white wine vinegar

¼ cup shallots, sliced

4 (4 ounce) salmon fillets

Sea salt for seasoning

Fresh ground pepper for seasoning

½ cup heavy cream

3 tablespoons fresh parsley, chopped

In skillet over low heat, cook white wine and shallots for 3 minutes. Season salmon with salt and pepper, add to skillet. Cover and cook over low heat for 10 minutes, turning salmon fillets after 5 minutes, until salmon reaches a safe internal temperature of 145°F. Remove salmon; keep warm. Add heavy cream to skillet; cook over high heat until reduced by half. Add chopped parsley and pour sauce over salmon fillets. Serve warm.

Chicken Enchiladas

4-6 large chicken breasts, cooked and shredded

½ cup sour cream

1 (8 ounce) cream cheese, softened

3 tablespoons canned chopped jalapeño peppers (or chilies)

1 tablespoon *Fuddruckers* seasoning

1 tablespoon fresh cilantro, chopped

3 cups Monterrey Jack cheese, shredded, divided

1 cup Cheddar cheese, shredded

2 dozen flour tortillas

Preheat oven to 375°F. Shred cooked chicken breasts and set aside. In mixing bowl, blend sour cream and cream cheese until smooth and creamy. Add peppers, *Fuddruckers* seasoning, and cilantro. Fold in 2 cups Monterrey Jack cheese and Cheddar cheese until well blended. Add shredded chicken, mix well. Spread 2 to 3 tablespoons chicken cream cheese mixture onto each tortilla and roll up. Place in greased 9x13 baking dish. Top with sauce, cover and bake for 30 minutes. Uncover and top with remaining Monterrey Jack cheese. Bake an additional 10 minutes until cheese is bubbly and golden brown. Note: *Fuddruckers* seasoning is a combination of paprika, black pepper, salt, dark brown sugar, garlic powder, onion powder, and cayenne pepper.

SAUCE FOR TOP:

½ cup butter

¼ cup flour

2 cups chicken broth

1 cup sour cream

Salt and pepper to taste

In sauce pan over medium heat, melt butter. Whisk in flour until incorporated. Slowly whisk in chicken broth and cook until bubbly and thick. Remove from heat, mix in sour cream. Salt and pepper to taste. Spoon over enchiladas and bake.

Salads and Sides

Mimi's Broccoli Salad

4 cups broccoli, chopped

1 cup celery, thin sliced

½ cup scallions, thinly sliced

4 bacon slices, cooked and crumbled

1 cup red and green grapes, halved

1 cup mayonnaise

½ cup sugar

2 teaspoons apple cider vinegar

Salt and pepper to taste

1½ cups sliced almonds, toasted

In large mixing bowl, combine first five ingredients, set aside. Using a small bowl, blend mayonnaise, sugar, and vinegar. Mix until smooth. Pour over broccoli mixture and toss to incorporate. Salt and Pepper as needed. Chill for 2 to 3 hours. Before serving top with sliced almond.

Bibb Salad with Raspberry Dressing

4 tablespoons Raspberry vinegar

2 tablespoons maple syrup

⅔ cup olive oil

1 head Bibb lettuce, washed and torn

1 small purple onion, sliced

1 (3 ounce) package Blue cheese, crumbled

3 tablespoons pine nuts, toasted

In small bowl, whisk vinegar, maple syrup, and oil. Chill. Arrange Bibb lettuce in salad bowl. Place sliced onion and Blue cheese crumbles on lettuce. Sprinkle pine nuts on top, drizzle with dressing and serve. Note: Substitute almonds, pecans, or walnuts for pine nuts.

Mixed Vegetable Salad

1 (1 pound) bunch broccoli, chopped

1 small head cauliflower, chopped

2 medium carrots, peeled and sliced thin

1 medium purple onion, thinly sliced

1 medium-size green pepper, cut into 1-inch pieces

1 (15 ounce) can garbanzo beans, drained

1 cup ripe olives, sliced (Optional)

1 (8 ounce) favorite vinaigrette dressing

Remove leaves and chop broccoli and cauliflower. Wash and pat dry. In large mixing bowl, combine broccoli and cauliflower florets with remaining ingredients, toss gently. Cover and chill at least 1 hour.

Spinach Salad

1 pound fresh spinach

1 apple, unpeeled, cored and sliced

2 tablespoons lemon juice

3 green onions, sliced

1 (2 ounce) package sliced almonds, toasted

3 slices of bacon, cooked and crumbled (Optional)

⅓ cup canola oil

⅓ cup red wine vinegar

2 to 3 teaspoons sugar

¾ teaspoon dry mustard

½ teaspoon salt

¼ teaspoon pepper

Remove stems from spinach; wash leaves thoroughly and pat dry. Tear into bite-size pieces. Toss apple slices in lemon juice; drain. Combine spinach, apple wedges, green onions, and almonds; toss with bacon if desired. Combine oil and remaining ingredients in jar with tight fitting lid. Cover tightly and shake vigorously. Chill. Before serving pour dressing over spinach and toss.

Becky's Salad

SALAD:

1 bag Romain lettuce, torn

¼ cup cranberries

1 Granny Smith apple, cubed

1 pear, cubed

1 (4 ounce) Swiss cheese, shredded

1 cup nut of choice, toasted

DRESSING:

⅔ cup olive oil

⅓ cup lemon juice

½ cup sugar

1 teaspoon Dijon mustard

2 teaspoons onion, finely minced

½ teaspoon salt

1 tablespoon poppy seed

Night before serving salad, mix dressing and refrigerate. Combine oil, and next six ingredients in jar with tight fitting lid. Shake vigorously and store in refrigerator. When ready to serve, place lettuce, cranberries, apple, pear, cheese and nuts in bowl, mix thoroughly. Drizzle with dressing and toss. Note: Dressing can be served on the side.

Pear and Arugula Salad with Goat Cheese

4 tablespoons olive oil

Juice of 1 lemon

Salt and fresh ground pepper

2 ripe pears, Bartlett or Anjou, cored,
and thinly sliced

6 ounces Arugula

½ cup Goat cheese, crumbled

⅓ cup walnuts, chopped and toasted

In small bowl, whisk together oil and lemon juice. Season to taste with salt and pepper. Set aside. Place pears in a large bowl. Whisk the olive oil and lemon again, and pour over pears, tossing gently to combine. Add Arugula and toss to gently distribute the ingredients. Divide evenly between four salad plates. Garnish with crumbled Goat cheese and walnuts.

Joy's Cheesy French Bread

1 loaf French bread

2 sticks butter, melted

2 tablespoons parsley

½ teaspoon marjoram, thyme, and tarragon

6 green onions, chopped

12 ripe olives, chopped fine

Preheat oven to 350°F. Slice loaf in half. Lay open on a large baking sheet. Brush halves with melted butter. In bowl, mix spices. Spread onions and olives along one half of the bread. Sprinkle spices over onions and olives. Fold halves and wrap loaf in foil. Bake for 15 to 20 until warm.

Cashew Green Beans

3 pounds fresh green beans

Water/Salt

1 stick butter

2 teaspoons lemon juice

1 cup cashews

Salt and pepper to taste

Trim ends off green beans. Bring large pot of salted water to a boil. Add beans, bringing water back to a slow boil. Cook uncovered for 8 to 12 minutes until crisp-tender. Plunge beans in ice water to stop cooking process and drain. Over medium heat, melt butter in skillet. Add beans, lemon juice, and cashews. Cook stirring completely for 10 to 15 minutes. Season with salt and pepper before serving.

Roasted Rosemary Potatoes

2 pounds potatoes, Red or Yukon

½ cup olive oil

2 tablespoons fresh rosemary, chopped

½ teaspoon nutmeg

Salt and pepper to taste

Preheat oven to 425°F. Quarter potatoes and parboil until just barely tender. Drain and place in a roasting pan. Add olive oil, rosemary, nutmeg, salt and pepper. Roast potatoes, turning occasionally, until tender and browned. Place in serving dish and drizzle seasoned oil from pan over potatoes. Note: Parboil is cooking by boiling.

Roasted Broccoli with Orange Chipotle Butter

2 (12 ounce) packages of fresh broccoli florets

2 tablespoons olive oil

¼ cup butter, soft

3 teaspoons orange rind, grated

1 teaspoon garlic, minced

2 tablespoons canned Chipotle peppers in adobe sauce

½ teaspoon salt

Preheat oven to 450°F. In bowl, toss broccoli florets and oil. Place on a jelly roll baking sheet and roast for 15 to 17 minutes until crisp-tender. While broccoli roast, in large bowl, combine butter, orange rind, garlic, Chipotle peppers, and salt. Add roasted broccoli to bowl and toss to coat. Serve hot.

Pear and Pistachio Baked Acorn Squash

2 acorn squash

2 teaspoons Canola oil

¼ teaspoon sea salt

¼ teaspoon ground pepper

1 cup Pistachio nuts, roasted and chopped

1 red D'Auou pear, cored and diced

2 teaspoons olive oil

2 teaspoons maple syrup

2 teaspoons red wine vinegar

2 sprigs rosemary, finely chopped

10 mint leaves, finely chopped

4 sprigs thyme, finely chopped

¼ teaspoon sea salt

¼ teaspoon ground pepper

Preheat oven to 400°F. Slice squash in half vertically and remove seeds. Place squash cut side up on rimmed baking sheet. Rub with oil and salt and pepper. Roast 30 to 35 minutes, or until soft. In medium bowl, mix together pear, oil, maple syrup, vinegar, herbs, salt and pepper. Divide filling among squash halves. Sprinkle with finely chopped Pistachio nuts. Place squash under broiler for 3 minutes, until golden. Serve warm.

Penne Pasta with Gorgonzola Cream Sauce

¼ cup unsalted butter

¾ cup heavy cream

¼ pound Gorgonzola cheese

1 (8 ounce) cream cheese

Salt and pepper to taste

1 pound Penne pasta

½ cup walnuts, chopped and toasted

1 teaspoon freshly ground nutmeg

Cook pasta according to package, tender but firm to the bite, until opaque. In saucepan on low heat, melt butter. Add cream, cream cheese, and Gorgonzola. Cook until cheeses melt, stirring continually. Season with salt and pepper. In large pot toss Penne with cream sauce. Serve warm garnished with walnuts and nutmeg.

Asparagus Bundles

1 pound fresh asparagus, trimmed

3 thin slices Prosciutto, cut in 1-inch strips

1 tablespoon olive oil

¼ teaspoon salt

⅛ teaspoon fresh ground pepper

2 tablespoons roasted red pepper, chopped

½ cup Goat or Feta cheese, crumbled

Preheat oven to 450°F. Line a 15x10x1 baking pan with parchment paper; set aside. Wrap asparagus spears in bundles with one strip of Prosciutto around middle. Place bundles is a single layer in parchment-lined pan. Drizzle with olive oil. Sprinkle with salt and pepper; top with roasted peppers. Bake 8 to 10 minutes or until asparagus is crisp tender. Sprinkle with cheese. Continue baking 5 minutes or until cheese is softened and heated through.

Balsamic Glazed Pesto Grilled Squash

1½ pounds yellow squash and zucchini, sliced diagonally, ½-inch thick ovals

2 teaspoons kosher salt, plus ¼ teaspoon

1 cup fresh basil leaves, packed

¼ cup extra virgin olive oil, plus 2 tablespoons

3 tablespoons Parmesan cheese, grated

1 clove garlic

¼ cup pine nuts, plus extra for garnish

Balsamic glaze for garnish

Fire up the grill to high heat. In colander, toss the squash and zucchini with 2 teaspoons of salt, drain for 30 minutes. Set aside. Process ¼ teaspoon salt, basil, ¼ cup olive oil, cheese, garlic, and pine nuts in a blender or food processor until smooth. Toss the squash and zucchini with 2 tablespoons olive oil. Grill for 2 to 4 minutes per side, until golden brown and tender. Top with pesto and drizzle with balsamic glaze and a sprinkle of pine nuts.

Joy's Squash Casserole

4 cups yellow squash, cooked crisp

½ cup onion, finely chopped

1½ cups Cheddar cheese, shredded, divided

2 cups cracker crumbs

⅔ cup half and half

2 eggs

½ stick butter, melted

Salt and pepper to taste

In small bowl, whisk half and half with eggs. Add melted butter, set aside. In large bowl, place squash, onion, 1 cup cheese, and cracker crumbs, mixing well. Pour half and half with eggs over squash mixture. Blend together. Pour into 9x13 baking dish, top with ½ cup Cheddar cheese and bake for 30 minutes until golden brown.

Potatoes Au Gratin

1 teaspoon olive oil

3 medium baking potatoes, sliced thin

3 tablespoons flour

1 medium onion, sliced thin in rings

⅛ teaspoon cayenne pepper

1 teaspoon paprika

½ teaspoon ground pepper

¼ teaspoon nutmeg

½ teaspoon seasoning salt

3 tablespoons Parmesan cheese, grated

1½ cups half and half

2 tablespoons fresh parsley, chopped

Preheat oven to 400°F. Coat baking dish with olive oil. Layer ⅓ potatoes in bottom, sprinkle 1 tablespoon flour over potatoes and top with onion rings. In small bowl, mix all dry seasonings and Parmesan. Sprinkle lightly with seasoning mix. Repeat layers until done. Pour half and half over potatoes and top with ¾ cup grated Cheddar cheese. Bake covered for 45 minutes, uncovered for additional 10 minutes. Garnish with parsley.

Pat's Corn Casserole

1 (8 ounce) package cream cheese, softened

½ stick butter, melted

¼ cup half and half

1 (10 ounce) bag Shoe peg corn

1 (4 ounce) can Rotel chilies, drain

1 teaspoon garlic powder

Salt and pepper to taste

Preheat oven to 350° F. In mixing bowl, blend cream cheese and butter until smooth. Add half and half, stir until blended. Add remaining ingredients into butter mixture and mix well. Pour into buttered 9x13 baking pan. Salt and pepper to taste. Bake for 20 to 25 minutes until heated through.

Desserts

Paulette's Chocolate Cake

SIFT TOGETHER:

3 cups all-purpose flour

2 cups sugar

2 teaspoons baking soda

½ teaspoon salt

½ cup cocoa powder

ADD:

2 cups water

2 tablespoons vinegar

1 cup canola oil

2 teaspoons vanilla

Preheat oven to 350°F. Shift dry ingredients into a large mixing bowl. Combine water, vinegar, oil, and vanilla to dry ingredients. Blend well. Grease a 9x13 pan. Pour batter into pan. Bake for 20 to 25 minutes. Cool and ice.

Light Yellow Cake

2½ cups cake flour

1½ teaspoons baking powder

¼ teaspoon baking soda

¾ teaspoon salt

1¾ cups sugar, divided

1¼ cups butter, melted and cooled

1 cup buttermilk, room temperature

3 tablespoons oil

2 teaspoons vanilla

6 large egg yolks, room temperature

3 large egg whites, room temperature

Preheat oven to 350°F. Separate the eggs while cold and set aside until room temperature. Grease and flour two 9-inch pans. In a large bowl, whisk flour, baking powder, baking soda, salt, and 1½ cups sugar. In separate bowl, mix butter, buttermilk, oil, vanilla and yolks until well blended. With whisk attachment on mixer whip egg whites and ¼ cup sugar until stiff peaks form, 30 to 60 seconds. Set aside. Slowly combine flour and butter mixture together, stopping and scraping sides. Once well blended, gently fold in egg whites. Pour batter into prepared pans and bake for 20 minutes. Cool on rack.

Chocolate Butter Cream Icing

1 (9 ounce) package semi-sweet chocolate chips

3 sticks butter, soft

2 tablespoons half and half

1 teaspoon vanilla

2¼ cups confectioners' sugar

Melt chocolate chips in microwave according to package instructions. Cool. In mixing bowl, whip butter until light and fluffy. Blend in chocolate until creamy. Add half and half and vanilla until smooth. Slowly add confectioners' sugar and mix until spreadable consistency.

Nell's Fresh Apple Cake

1½ cups flour

1 cup sugar

1 teaspoon salt

1 teaspoon baking soda

1 teaspoon nutmeg

1½ teaspoons cinnamon

¾ cup oil

2 eggs, room temperature

2 teaspoons vanilla extract

1 teaspoon almond extract

3 cups apples, finely chopped

1 cup nuts, chopped

In mixing bowl, place all dry ingredients. Mix on low until blended. In separate bowl place oil, eggs, vanilla extract, and almond extract, mix until smooth. Slowly add in flour mixture. Fold in apples and nuts. Pour batter into ungreased 6½x10x2 baking pan. Bake for 45 minutes. Once cool, dust with mixture of cinnamon and confectioners' sugar.

Grandmother's Plum Cake

2 cups self-rising flour

2 cups sugar

2 teaspoons cinnamon

1 teaspoon ground cloves

1 cup oil

3 eggs, room temperature

2 small jars of plum baby food

Preheat oven at 350°F. In large bowl, mix all dry ingredients until well incorporated. Stir in oil, eggs, and baby food. Pour into 9x13 greased and floured pan. Bake for 30 to 40 minutes.

Blueberry Pound Cake

2 cups granulated sugar

½ cup butter, softened

1 (8 ounce) cream cheese, softened

3 large eggs, room temperature

1 large egg white, room temperature

3 cups flour, divided

2 cups fresh blueberries

1 teaspoon baking powder

½ teaspoon baking soda

½ teaspoon salt

1 (8 ounce) carton lemon yogurt

2 teaspoons vanilla

½ cup powdered sugar

4 teaspoons lemon

Preheat oven to 350°F. Beat first 3 ingredients at medium speed until well-blended. Add eggs and egg white, one at a time, beating well after each addition. Lightly spoon flour into dry measuring cups; level with knife. Combine 2 tablespoons flour and blueberries in a small bowl. Combine remaining flour, baking powder, baking soda, and salt. Add flour mixture to sugar mixture alternately with yogurt, beginning and ending with flour mixture. Fold in blueberry mixture and vanilla; pour cake batter into a greased and floured 10-inch tube pan or Bundt pan. Bake for one hour and ten minutes or until wood pick inserted in center comes out clean. Cool cake for ten minutes then remove from pan. Combine powdered sugar and lemon juice in small bowl; drizzle over warm cake.

Mahogany Chocolate Pound Cake

1 cup butter, softened

2 cups sugar

1 cup brown sugar, firmly packed

6 eggs, separated, room temperature

2½ cups all-purpose flour

½ cup cocoa

1 cup sour cream

¼ teaspoon baking soda

2 teaspoons vanilla

Cream butter; gradually add sugars, beating well at medium speed of an electric stand mixer. Add egg yolks, one at a time, beating after each addition. Sift flour and cocoa together. Combine sour cream and baking soda. Add flour mixture to creamed mixture alternately with sour cream, beginning and ending with flour mixture. Mix just until blended after each addition. Stir in vanilla. Beat ½ cup sugar and egg whites until stiff peaks form; fold into batter. Spoon batter into greased and floured 10-inch tube pan. Bake for 1 hour and fifteen minutes until wood pick inserted in center comes out clean. Cool in pan 10 minutes; remove from pan, and let cool completely on wire rack. <u>Optional</u>: Add one cup of chocolate chips coated with 1 tablespoon of flour into batter before turning into tube pan to bake.

Spiced Apple Bundt Cake

2 boxes Duncan Hines Spice cake mix

2 eggs, room temperature

3 egg whites, room temperature

1 (21 ounce) can apple pie filling

4 teaspoons confectioners' sugar

Preheat oven to 350°F. Grease and flour 10-inch Bundt pan. In large bowl with electric mixer on low speed, beat cake mix, apple filling, egg yolks, and egg whites until moistened. Pour batter into pan. Bake for 40 to 45 minutes or until wood pick inserted comes out clean. Completely cool in pan on wire rack. Remove from pan and once cool, dust with cinnamon and confectioners' sugar.

Easy Lemon Cookies

COOKIE:

1 (15.25 ounce) box lemon cake mix

2 eggs, room temperature

¼ cup canola oil

2 tablespoons lemon juice

1 tablespoon lemon zest

½ teaspoon vanilla

GLAZE:

1 cup confectioners' sugar

2 tablespoons lemon juice

¼ teaspoon vanilla

Preheat oven to 350°F. Line two baking sheets with parchment paper. Add all cookie ingredients to large mixing bowl, and beat on medium with electric mixer until smooth, about 2 minutes. Using scoop, drop cookie dough in 12 heaping tablespoons about 1½ inches apart on each baking sheet. Bake for 8 to 10 minutes, until tops look dry and don't wiggle when you shake them. Let cool 5 minutes before transferring to cooling rack. While cookies cool, make glaze, if desired. Whisk together confectioners' sugar, lemon juice, and vanilla. Drizzle glaze on cookies and allow to harden 10 to 15 minutes.

ACKNOWLEDGEMENTS

Marge Lenow

————

My friend and mentor without whose little red pen and hundreds
of invested hours, this work would not have been completed.

Tyler Bedwell

————

The sweetest and most gifted graphic artist I know.
What a treasure you are to me and this ministry.

Will Porada

————

Your love of photography and for capturing the moment is reflected in your work.

Ashley Berry, Macy Cross, Julie Foreman, and Libby Phillips

————

A dynamic team of young women who believed and invested in this ministry
from day one. I could not have done it without your valuable input and support.

*Linda Horn, Donna Gaines, Carol Smith, Ginger Calcote,
Ellen Olford, Tim Whitehorn, and Mark Spiller*

————

I am grateful for your willingness to serve on our ministry board
—for your wisdom, knowledge, talent, and love of this ministry.

To the young women who have participated in the Secrets Savored Ministry

————

I love you and count it a joy to watch God lengthen your cords,
and strengthen your stakes for His glory! (Isaiah 54:2).

*To the many mature women who have invested their lives
in community with young women*

———

Thank you for stepping up and sacrificially obeying God's mandate in
Titus 2 to pour your lives into the lives of young women—you are to be honored.

To my Grands—all seven

———

What an unbelievable treasure you are. Each uniquely different
and bringing more joy to my life than I could have ever imagined!

To my Daughters and Sons-in Law

———

You have made me very proud.
I am grateful for the privilege of being your mom!

To my life mate, Mark, who now resides in Heaven

———

Without his love, counsel, support, and prayers, I would not be
the woman I am today. It was painful to watch him suffer.
But early on in our journey, God gave me a promise in Jeremiah 30:17
to completely restore Mark—and He kept His promise.
Babe, you were my joy. You were my undeserved gift from my loving
heavenly Father. I will always treasure our 45 years!

I loved you to the moon and back.

BIBLE TRANSLATIONS

1. Scripture quotations marked AMP are taken from *Amplified Bible*, copyright © 2015 by The Lockman Foundation, La Habra, CA 90631. All rights reserved. For permission to quote information visit http://www.lockman.org/

2. Scripture quotations marked CSB are taken from the *Christian Standard Bible*®, Copyright © 2017 by Holman Bible Publishers. For permission to quote *Christian Standard Bible*®, and CSB® are federally registered trademarks of Holman Bible Publishers.

3. Scripture quotations marked ESV are taken from The Holy Bible, *English Standard Version*, copyright © 2001 by Crossway Bibles, a division of Good News Publishers. Used by permission. All rights reserved.

4. *God's Word Translation* is a copyrighted work of God's Word to the Nations. Quotations and used by permission. Copyright 1995 by God's Word to the Nations. All rights reserved.

5. Scripture quotations marked HCSB are taken from the *Holman Christian Standard Bible*®, Copyright © 1999, 2000, 2002, 2003, 2009 by Holman Bible Publishers. Used by permission. Holman Christian Standard Bible®, Holman CSB®, and HCSB® are federally registered trademarks of Holman Bible Publishers.

6. Scripture taken from the *International Children's Bible*®. Copyright © 1986, 1988, 1999 by Thomas Nelson. Used by permission. All rights reserved.

7. Scripture taken from the Holy Bible: *International Standard Version*®. Copyright © 1996, forever by The ISV Foundation. ALL RIGHTS RESERVED INTERNATIONALLY. Used by permission.

8. Scripture taken from the *New American Standard Bible*®, Copyright © 1960, 1962, 1963, 1968, 1971, 1972, 1973, 1975, 1977, 1995 by Lockman Foundation. Used by permission.

9. Scripture quotations marked (NIRV) are taken from the Holy Bible, *New International Reader's Version*®, NIRV® Copyright © 1995, 1996, 1998, 2014 by Biblica, Inc.™ Used by permission of Zondervan.

10. Scripture quotations marked NIV are taken from the Holy Bible, *New International Version*®. Copyright © 1973, 1978, 1984 by International Bible Society. Used by permission of Zondervan. All rights reserved.

11. Scripture quotations marked NKJV are taken from the Holy Bible, are taken from *The New King James Version*. Copyright © 1982, by Thomas Nelson, Inc. Used by permission. All rights reserved.

12. Scripture quotations marked NLT are taken from the Holy Bible, *NLT Parallel Study Bible-New Living Translation*. Copyright © 1996, 2004, 2007 by Tyndale House Publications. Used by Tyndale House Publishing, Inc., Carol Stream, Illinois 60188. All rights reserved worldwide.

13. Scripture quotations are from *New Revised Standard Version Bible*, copyright © 1989 National Council of the Churches of Christ in the United States of America. Used by permission. All rights reserved worldwide.

14. Scripture quotations marked NLV are taken from the Holy Bible, *New Life Version*, Copyright © 1969-2003 by Christian Literature International, P.O. Box 777, Canby, Oregon 97013. Used by permission.

15. Scripture quotations marked TLB are taken from *The Living Bible* Copyright ©1971. Used by permission by Tyndale House Publishing, Inc., Carol Stream, Illinois 60188. All rights reserved.

16. Scripture taken from *The Message*, Copyright © 1993, 1994, 1995, 1996, 2000, 2001, 2002. Used by permission of NavPress Publishing Group.

Dianne Dougharty was married to her high school sweetheart for forty-five years. After an extended illness, Mark went to be with Jesus on July 31, 2018. She is the mother of two daughters and Mimi to seven grandchildren. Dianne graduated from Trevecca Nazarene University with a degree in Elementary Education. For over twenty years, she has led women's Bible studies, spoken at conferences, authored curriculum, and contributed written work to several blogs. She faithfully served for years beside her husband in full-time vocational ministry.

Dianne has a desire to see older women fulfill the mandate given them in Titus 2:3-4, "These older women must train the younger women to love their husbands and their children, to live wisely and be pure, to work in their homes, to do good, and to be submissive to their husbands. Then they will not bring shame to the word of God" (NLT).

Her heart is for young women to become seekers of Christ, students of God's Word, and lovers of their home, husband, family, and calling. She has a passion to see women live purposefully—making investments in the lives of other women.

God led Dianne to develop the Secrets Savored Ministry, a fun hands-on approach to developing community among women who desire to create a spirit of hospitality and Christlikeness within their lives, homes, and relationships—for the glory of God! Once a week, small groups meet within home settings and learn to apply biblical principles for living a godly life in an often God-less world.

Check out the ministry at secretssavored.org.
Follow her on Facebook, Twitter, and Pinterest.

Secrets Savored

PARTICIPATION INFO SHEET

NAME: _____

SINGLE: _____

MARRIED: 1–5 years _____ 6–10 years _____ More than 10 years _____

AGE: 15–22 _____ 23–30 _____ 31–35 _____ over 35 _____

E-MAIL: _____

ADDRESS: _____

_____

_____

CELL PHONE: _____

WORK PHONE: _____

ALLERGIES: _____

Tell us about yourself: Example: Where did you go to school? Where do you work? Where did you grow up? Do you have any unusual life experiences? Do you have any children? If so, how many and what are their ages

CREATING COMMUNITY

SECRETS *Savored*

THROUGH SIMPLE HOSPITALITY

Secrets Savored is a Titus 2 discipling tool. Women across generations discover the treasure of community as they practice simple hospitality and apply Biblical truths in a home setting. This in-depth Bible study is growing women into a deeper faith and building Christ-like character within them.

CONNECT WITH US @SECRETSSAVORED

Books are available for purchase as eBook. Visit secretssavored.org to order.

Made in the USA
Coppell, TX
05 July 2022